NEUROTHEOLOGY

NEUROTHEOLOGY

Virtual Religion
in the
21st Century

LAURENCE O.
MCKINNEY

American Institute for Mindfulness
Box 390309
Cambridge, MA 02139-0004

9   8   7   6   5   4   3   2   1

First Edition
Printed in the United States of America
Distributed in the United States by
Golly

LIBRARY OF CONGRESS NUMBER

94-076877

ISBN   0-945724-01-4

Book Design and Typesetting
Deborah Bourienne

Cover Design
Karma Dodrup Dorje

Portrait of Laurence O. McKinney
Pedersen

To my mother,
Betsy Marvin McKinney Strain,
whose vibrant interest in religion and
medicine, as well as writing and media,
provided the earliest foundations of
my own fascination and involvement, and
without whose support this
book could never
have been completed.

CONTENTS

Acknowledgements   i

Preface   v

Part One: Introduction

1   Preparing for the Coming Faithquake   3
     Faith Tectonics and New World Religions

2   The Metaphysics of Neuroscience   19
     Paradigms for Consciousness

3   Virtually Real   31
     Painting by Numbers

Part Two: The Past

4   In the Beginning   51
     From Heaven to Earth

5   Stranded in the Here and Now   65
     The Evolution of Chronology

Part Three: The Present

6   Only Now   89
     Abstraction, Projection, and Time

7   Feel is How We Real   99
    The Meaning of It All

8   Energy and Ecstasy   117
    Rats, Rapture, and Religion

Part Four: The Future

9   Priests and Prophets   139
    Fulfillment in Real Time

10 Soul Survivors   155
    What Really Happens When We Die

ACKNOWLEDGEMENTS

The work that became *Neurotheology* got its start in 1976 and was finished in 1994. It went through five titles, two literary agents, and the heads of nearly everyone I knew. There are parts that date to that first version, and at least one major concept appears first in the 1994 volume. It was a steady evolution.

No one person could be expert in the many fields represented in this work. My advantage as an amateur was that I was able to cross many boundaries, but it left me completely dependent on the expertise of others. *Neurotheology* was a one person project, but it is synthesized from the wisdom and teaching I received from an extraordinary group of people.

First the muses, catalysts between skill and art because we write for some person, always. Years after when it is finally reworked and polished and published we never forget. *Neurotheology* began with the helpful enthusiasm of Marianne Habib Arling and was completed when Alexandra Scott Masand took an interest. My studies at Harvard Divinity School and later with Shubha Shankaran, Thupten Kalsang, and the Dalai Lama were the beneficial results of their natural love of religion, music, neurology, and Asian culture. Special thanks are also due to neurophysiologist Jonathan B.B. Earle who for many years kept me anchored safely within the boundaries of real neuroscience. The others include the following.

Manuscript Readers: Marianne Habib Arling, Sigalit Avigdory, Elizabeth Backman, Peter Caulfield, Nike Caulfield, Arthur C. Clarke, Harvey Cox, Candida Donadio, Jonathan B.B. Earle, Elissa Ely, Julia Geanakakis, Mollie Geismer, Prabha S. Guha, Suzanne Kammlott, Adele Leone, Kim Kadohata Maire, Andrew McKinney, Susan Lyden Murphy,

Raquel Ojeda, Bill Pedersen, John Pepple, Susanna Porter, Upendra J.B.S. Rana, Cristina Sanmartin, Bob Silverstein, Peter Skolnik, Betsy Marvin McKinney Strain, Jeremy Tarcher, Deborah Ullman.

Darshan

From college classrooms to brief meetings, from a letter to a conversation, each of the following individuals spoke or wrote to me directly, teaching me something I never forgot, although the circumstances were often not what one might expect. I knew Beverly Sills as Mrs. Peter Greenough, stepmother of a college girlfriend, Mother Theresa was just hanging around at the Delhi Airport, and Robert Frost visited my prep school. I worked for Leo Fender one summer, greeted the elderly Erik Erikson on the sidewalk, and discovered Paul Samuelson behind me in line at my bank, of course. Some, like Harvey Cox and Leonard Nash, were important teachers and the Dalai Lama is my guru. I lent my guitar to Del Shannon, and my ear to Chuck Berry in a dressing room. I sneaked into neurology classes by Jerome Katz at Harvard Medical School when I wasn't enrolled. My favorite writer, Annie Dillard, gave me about twenty seconds, Norman Mailer gave me about the same, Arthur C. Clarke broke his own rules to read and comment on my very first version, and even Anais Nin, radiant in her sixties, had something to tell me about writing. In nearly every instance I was able to say "thank you," and I remember each contact as if it were yesterday. Thank you all, again. There is something of each of you in this work.

Writers: Tsultrim Allione, John Blofeld, William F. Buckley, Jr., Fritjof Capra, Carlos Castaneda, Arthur C. Clarke, Cid Corman, Gregory Corso, Edwin Bernbaum, Elissa Ely, Annie Dillard, Robert Frost, Norman Mailer, Marianne Moore, Anais Nin, William Novak, Camille Paglia, Allen Tate, Hunter Thompson, Elizabeth Winship.

Religion and Philosophy: Steven Bachelor, Baghwan Das (Michael Riggs), Alexander Berzin, Sri Chinmoy, Chung Hyun-Kyung, Harvey Cox, Archibishop Dimitrios, Diana Eck, Jeffrey Hopkins, L. Ron Hubbard, Pir Vilayat Khan, Timothy Leary, George McRae, Maharishi Mahesh Yogi, Masatoshi Nagatomi, Richard Reinhardt Neibuhr, Ram Das, Swami Rama, Mother Theresa, Robert F. Thurman, Paul Tillich, Desmond Tutu, Helen Tworkov.

Tibetans: Chetsang Rinpoche, Chogyam Trungpa Rinpoche, The 14th Dalai Lama, Dodrup Chen Rinpoche, Jetsun Dolma Rinpoche, Thupten Kalsang Rinpoche, Kalu Rinpoche, The Gyalwa Karmapa, Lati Rinpoche, Tipu Tulku.

Science, Medicine and Psychology: Freed Bales, Deepak Chopra, Christine De LaCoste, Erik Erikson, Roland Fisher, Elmer Green, Lester Grinspoon, Stanislav Grof, David Hubel, Jerome Katz, Everett Koop, Salvatore Luria, Benoit Mandelbrot, Margaret Mead, Roy Menninger, Leonard Nash, Seymour Papert, Norman Ramsey, Arthur Sackler, Carl Sagan, Richard Evans Schultes, Alexander Shulgin, B.F. Skinner, George Vaillant, George Wald, Andrew Weil, E.O. Wilson, Norman E. Zinberg.

Scholars: William Alfred, John Fairbank, John Kenneth Galbraith, Herman Khan, Mario Laserna, Jagdish Parikh, Daniel Pipes, Edwin Reischauer, Miranda Shaw.

Musicians: Nikil Bannerjee, Chuck Berry, Hari Prasad Charausia, Dick Dale, Dave Guard, Emmy Lou Harris, Zakir Hussein, Ali Akbar Khan, Vilayat Khan, Imrat Khan, Arvind Parikh, Nick Reynolds, Pete Seeger, Bob Shane, Ravi Shankar, Del Shannon (Charles Westover), Beverly Sills, Link Wray.

Business and Economics: Hobie Alter, Amar Bose, John Fan, Leo Fender, Christy Hefner, Mitch Kapor, James Ling, Ralph Lowell, Anita Roddick, Jack Ryan, James A. Ryder, Ernesto Samper, Paul Samuelson, Renato Tagiuri, Lester Thurow, Dewey Weber, Mortimer Zuckerman.

Others: Mohammad Ali, Sidney Biddle Barrows, Queen Beatrix, Edward Bernays, King Birendra, Stockard Channing, Tucker Clark, Princess Christina, Archibald Cox, Rennie Davis, Allan Dershowitz, Fred Glimp, Daniel Goleman, Morey Grebb, Johnny Hart, Abbie Hoffman, Ismail Merchant, John Miller, Robert Morse, Martin Mull, William Munroe, Mira Nair, Prince Stobdan Namra, Jackie Onassis, Ashok Raj Pandy, Durga Pokhrel, Jerry Rubin, Karna Sakya, Daniel Samper, Al Smith, Oliver Stone, Garry Trudeau, Eric Utne, George Wallace, Jessie Whitehead . . . and the yogi at the sideshow. May all beings be happy; not one left behind.

PREFACE

I was always different. I never had a casual thought in my life; I pondered mysteries of life and death when I was a child. As far back as I can remember I wondered about death. I would look up at the great amber hanging lanterns in the church during Sunday services and wonder what would happen if one just dropped on me. I almost wished it would, just to find out. It seemed that nobody had the answer. I went to confirmation class because I thought Sally Meneely was cute; by then I had other things on my mind. Still, from about the age of nine, it had become my own life challenge. What was it really? What actually happened?

My father was a Harvard wit, who wrote light verse and ran the old family steel company, handling management while Maurice Roses ran the engineering. The firm began as a stove works, "McKinney & Abrams" back in 1857. It reincarnated as Albany Architectural Ironworks, won renown for fancy cast iron store fronts in the 1880's, and assumed its third life as James McKinney & Son when my grandfather entered the firm. My father was born in 1891 and I was born in his 54th year, the son of the son of the son of McKinney & Son and his wife, a 27 year old Emma Willard girl who did Swarthmore and R.A.D.A. He wrote a Hasty Pudding show, was Albany's major culture maven, never made much money, and died at 77 of Hodgkin's disease. They named the Albany Institute of History and Art library after him, and ran obits and editorials about him for a week or so.

When I was a child, every night when he came home from the plant (I once thought my father worked with vegetables and not at an office) where he "made money" (from long strips of copper with a penny die-out stamp I assumed), he would answer any three questions we had.

Anything at all. "Where does paint get color?" "From pigments, in a carrier base." I imagined colored pigs frolicking on the decks of aircraft carriers, safe at home in their naval base. He always had the answers.

Every spring the carnival came to town. *James E. Strates Shows* would arrive and pitch its tents in a huge field at the bottom of the Menands hill. They set up a midway, erected a fun house, the side show, the thrill riders, the coin tosses, cotton candy stands and rides that towered over our heads, each tethered to a snorting diesel generator with some wild kid at the controls. It was heaven to a ten year old with ten dollars to spend.

It was the yogi that I will never forget. With a blowtorch, he heated iron bars red hot and stepped on them; he blowtorched his own moustache and nothing singed. He stood on red-hot swords. The whites of his eyes were yellow. Too much heat, I figured. My mother stayed after the show; she wanted to know just how he did it. The yogi stepped forward, you could see he was weary. No, there was no trick; it was the result of a great deal of training. Here, he was just being paid to do it. "Of course," he said, "It will do me no good, the money. I have used my gifts for financial gain, this should never be done. There is no hope for me."

I looked into his tired eyes and they were like black marbles, shiny, lifeless, cold. A sudden chill gripped my mind; this man was telling me a truth. Special gifts are not gained to be used in a sideshow, money made in this way is worse than no money at all. I had met my first Eastern adept, and we communicated just fine; he was working in the sideshow and faithful to a system which could both empower and undo. I was still in cotton candy land, but I knew that he knew something I dearly wanted to know.

Twenty five years and many lifetimes later it all came back to me while I was working on the theoretical basis for the perception of chronology. If what seemed to be the case were in fact true, it could explain the secret of time. If one could do that, we could generate some real insights into the major metaphysical rules underlying all the world religions. It all made sense, but the conclusions were nearly frightening. I had lucked on to some real knowledge; I knew for sure now what happened in death and it had completely rearranged my understanding of life. Was this a gift, or a curse? I wished my father were around to ask, but he had died when I was only 22.

My mother lived another twenty six years. She was there when the firm went bankrupt and was sold to Mark Larner for the price of a parking lot. She had taught natural childbirth in the forties, natural foods in fifties, natural religion in the sixties; naturally always ahead of her time enough to be a natural amateur savant, without the patience to stay with anything long enough to win professional respect. She was self taught in medical matters, with several thousands of dollars worth of medical textbooks filled with underlines, highlights and margin notes. Her last preoccupation was her eventual stroke, a subject which kept her both stressed and stressful. At 75, she agreed to try some powerful meditative techniques I had learned directly from the Dalai Lama which included focussed mental imagery. It worked, she said, and claimed her trusty Holt blood pressure monitor even recorded it. A year later, she was gone.

After her first severe stroke, I read her CAT scans and was appalled at the devastation. Fully three fifths of her right hemisphere was gone for good. The attending neurologist said to expect the worst; no emotional affect and a foggy mind at best. The best thing, he said, would be another stroke. She was still having difficulty opening her eyes; one side of her body was limp as a rag. She was speaking sometimes in French, but she was coming back by the third day. I bent over her when she seemed lucid and said, "I checked your scans, Mom. You've lost a big chunk in the middle of the right hemisphere but your prefrontal lobes are fine and the visual cortex is still there." With her eyes still closed, she whispered "middle cerebral artery."

She was right of course. Then she asked, "Should I do my vipassana now?" I was floored. I had taught her to recall an image from memory and study it in the mind with the eyes closed. Even with such destruction, the teaching was intact and so was her logic. I gave her hand a squeeze. "Wonderful, Mom, it's great exercise for the visual cortex. That's just what you need now." Looking ahead, her eyes still closed, she said gravely, "What I need now is prayers."

She had read earlier drafts of this book, and she knew that we had what seemed to be the scientific answers for a number of very basic human questions. She had taken the original chapter on death to the dying, and had told me of their tears, sometimes, of relief when someone saw that the end, when it came, was a guaranteed heaven no matter what. My mother was religious, but for her the theories made sense, and she shared them with those whom she knew needed some faith without the religion.

Now, in the anticipation of her own death, my mother was slowly return-ing to the faith she had been born into.

She did not die of another stroke. She died a month later from bacte-rial and fungal infections which had been diagnosed but not adequately treated. It was as gentle a death as one could imagine as the pathogens slowly turned her brain to Kool Whip one cc. at a time. At the very end, the last day I knew she was there, she looked vacantly into my eyes. I looked deeply into hers, and there she was, like a person at the very bot-tom of a swimming pool. She was looking up, letting me know she was there but, honestly, very far away. It carried another message. "You were right; I'm in another place." Late that evening, I could feel her soul sighing into the night with the sounds of the late night traffic travers ing the long bridge in the distance. The next day she was flatlined. Her pacemaker had Energizer Bunny batteries, however, and so she stuck around for curtain calls. She was an actress, and she had the whole stage to herself. Like my father, she took a week and died, like him, less than a month before her 77th birthday. During that week she showed up in four different people's dreams.

"She said she was satisfied with her life, and generally pleased with the way her sons were getting along in life," said Prabha, an Indian neurolo-gist who had become a close friend and confidant during her last four years. "She said that there was one small disappointment, however; she was sorry that your book wasn't published." Even at that last lucid level of mental attachment to this world, she'd known I was trying to cheer her up but she hadn't let on, an actress to the end. The next month, Mark Larner finally gave up trying to stamp out pennies at the steel company he had bought for nickels, and the doors at James McKinney & Son, after 135 years, closed forever. It was over.

The book has been published now, or you wouldn't be reading it. Like my father, I wanted to answer a question for all the people; and by the time my mother died, the answers were in hand. At the end, she was comforted in her simple Christian faith and went, as Judy said, "to the arms of the Savior she knew and loved." I may well too; those are my earliest memories at Sunday school, long before I was interested in girls or metaphysics, and I'm not going to try to modify them. I know where I'm going, and whether it's called endless lifetimes or the life everlasting, it's not a bad trip at all. The big question was answered as far as I was concerned, and the rest of the book, as Rabbi Hillel joked, standing on one leg "is only commentary." In fact, the process of answering one difficult question required quite a lot more.

"Is it possible to describe a new, comprehensive philosophy of life that answers most of the major questions in six pages?" It was 1981 and I was still nervous about watching it all fall into place. "Sure," he said, "but you might need six hundred to explain just how you got there." It turned out that if we can agree to accept the concept of a mental virtual reality, we are now into an entire systematic philosophy based on neuroscience. That begins to explain these hundred and sixty-six pages and why *Neurotheology* is a lot more than the death experience. As to why it took another twelve years or so, it had to be rewritten a lot.

The final manuscript was almost ready when I saw psychologist B.F. Skinner ambling through Harvard Square one day. I knew that he was not well and it might be my last chance to ask him a good question. "Dr. Skinner," I started, "I was also an English major who got caught up in neurological detail. You once considered writing as a career. What effect did this have on your later work?" He smiled, and there was a real twinkle in his eye. "I have lived a long and predominantly rewarding life," he said, his words flowing in precise intonation, "And I have always taken it for granted that a large measure of my success was simply due to the fact that I could write a great deal better than most of my colleagues." I shared a big grin with him. If it was worth writing, if you had the gift, the art was as much as the science.

He died a few months later and in honor of the craft of writing, I wrote the whole thing over again just to polish it up. If I'd spent half a lifetime answering one question, there's no reason not to be elegant about it and put on the best show possible. This is an easy to read deep book; it took every bit of my writing skill and nothing will ever be that hard to do, or so rewarding to see completed. It's the best I'll ever do.

Neurotheology will make you think about things you never thought about before in ways you never thought you would think about them. That is my first promise. The second is that if someone gets the idea that this is a Western take on Eastern Philosophy, more exactly, some proofs of the Prasangika School of Mahadyamika Buddhism as promulgated by Nagarjuna, singly or eponymously, and developed by Chandrakirti, Shantideva, and Tsong Khapa, they might be on the right track. There is nothing new here; all real truths are ancient. We simply change the ex-

Preface

planations so that we can believe a little better whenever it's important to have a reason to believe. In these times, it's more important than ever.

The night I met the carnival yogi, I rode the Ferris wheel up into the night, and at the top, it stopped for a moment and if we looked down we could see the entire midway, sparkling and bustling, the games, the tents, the support trucks and supply vans, and behind them the fields, the high-way beyond, the Menands hill, and the starry sky reaching over our heads. It was very big and vast and then, suddenly, the diesel gives a snort, the ride goes forward, and we're back to cotton candy land again.

This is not a long book; but for some it will provide a new perspective, a Ferris wheel for the mind. At least that is my hope; and then back to the lights, the action, and all the games of life.

Part One:
Introduction

1

Preparing for the Coming Faithquake

Faith Tectonics and New World Religions

"If God had wanted it that way, He would have made you all of one religion, but He has done otherwise so to test you in the various ways He has given you. Therefore, press forward in good works; unto God shall you return and He will tell you about those areas in which you disagree."

—*The Koran*

There is a pressing problem facing mankind. It is based on the powerful effects of a global society on religious faiths which originate in differing cultural traditions. There is now a strong probability that the next fifty years will witness the emergence of new, scientifically based global "religions." Are we ready for this next step in our social evolution? Opinions differ, but the facts remain. Traditional religion may be the last casualty of the twentieth century, surviving in the form of cultural archives, greatly reduced in authority and influence.

It would hardly seem that way based on current trends. In 1991, 40% of those responding to a United States poll chose faith in God as "top priority." Twenty-nine percent chose good health and only 2% chose money, prompting Wade Clark Roof, Professor of Religion and Society at UCLA to write that such "astounding" numbers suggested a "cultural shift." Eighty-six point five percent of Americans responding to a survey commissioned by City University of New York declared themselves

Christian; however there also were over a million American Buddhists and a half million Hindus. That month the *New York Times* reported more Muslim pilgrims than ever before were flocking to Iran's holy shrines, expecting, as a devotee assured the reporters, that Mohammed would answer their prayers "100 percent!" By 1993, Christian fundamentalists in Vista, California elected enough candidates to a local school board to require the teaching of Bible based history. About two months later, a rabbi condemned a dairy in Jerusalem for suggesting dinosaurs on its milk cartons were millions of years old "despite the fact the world was created only 5,753 years ago." In Egypt that week, fundamentalists in Abu Zabaar prison were recruiting supporters when one of the thugs cursed Islam. The resulting brawl, which lasted three hours, left three dead and 85 wounded. Why are the devout getting so aggressive? Because they feel threatened, and they have plenty of reason to feel this way.

Even as the faithful gather together worldwide, the orderly integration of world religions, once limited by sheer physical distance, has gotten completely out of control. There are now more Muslims than Unitarians in the United States and the Mormons are expanding rapidly in Brazil. Evangelical Christianity is enjoying phenomenal growth in Korea, while Korean Sun Myung Moon, in America, preaches a married Christ who is himself. Japanese Buddhists teach Los Angelenos to chant the Lotus Sutra while German Neo-Hindus in saffron jhabalas chant Hare Krishna in Red Square, ignoring both the cold and the cold war between Russian Orthodox priests and Western tele-preachers bent on rustling their new-found flocks with heavy-metal hallelujah revivals.

It's open season for souls, it seems, but nobody has taken account of where this is all going to end up. To be frank, if human society does not come up with some generally acceptable world religions fairly soon, millions of people will needlessly suffer and perish in confrontations based on ancient religious disagreement. Sooner or later we will have to stop debating whose God is God and whose Holy Scriptures are the ones to trust. Theologians and philosophers are beginning to perspire noticeably as we near an inevitable spiritual showdown.

The Roots of Regional Religious Tradition

Sociobiologist E.O. Wilson believes massive climactic changes may have been behind the sociological phenomena of Western religions. At the Harvard Divinity School 175th anniversary in 1992, he described the desert-like Middle Eastern Biblical lands as lushly vegetated in recent prehistory, a true Garden of Eden. Rapid desertification of the region acted as a psychological shock wave, dislocating cultures and formalizing religion when oral traditions still spoke of a time when life was very different.

Likewise, intense cultural upheavals represented by the invasions of Aryans, Mongols, and Muslims had a similar effect on religious orientation in Asia and South Asia. Whole societies hungered for spiriual powers to counteract some very real fears. Major Hindu and Buddhist esoteric traditions, according to religious scholar Alexander Berzin, seemed to appear when it was important to find ways to unite differing peoples and castes to face some impending danger. When God only knows what's going to happen next, it's important to know ways to call on some higher powers for help.

As a result, all world religions originated in specific geographic locations with cultural traditions built in from the beginning. The Mediterranean basin was the cradle for early Christianity, which followed the Roman empire to Europe and then to the Americas. From the Arabian desert, Mohammed's message spread south and east from Africa to India, to Indonesia, Malaysia and the Philippines. The teachings of the Buddha traveled the trade routes south to Sri Lanka and Thailand and the silk roads East to Mongolia, China, and Japan. Lao Tzu and Confucius were both born in China, and their words went West against the flow of Hindus, Muslims, Buddhists, and Christians.

This slow spread of regional faiths on foot and primitive forms of transportation allowed large areas to become associated with one belief or another, a geographical religious homogeneity which lasted until the present. When differing faiths encountered each other there was usually either conversion or persecution. This required the de-humanization of minority non-believers, be they Inca, Jew, Mormon, or Moonie. Western faiths especially have problems with synthesis; fundamentalist Muslims vie with born-again Christians in us-versus-them theologies. In the East, mergers were tolerated, although sometimes uncomfortable. In the primal case of the uninvited dinner guest, the unruly South Indian dravidic deity Shiva, faced with the gradual encroachment of the grand new gods of the conquering Aryans, simply moved in with Brahma and Vishnu; trident, tantras, snakes and all.

As Christianity gradually worked its way into Europe, Celtic pagan religious feasts were resurfaced as Christian holidays while grottos, such as Lourdes, once dedicated to local female deities, became associated with the Virgin Mary. Animist mountain demons in the Himalayas were converted by Buddhist yogis into heroic "dharmapalas," guardians of the Dharma. The encroaching religion rarely totally usurped earlier beliefs; more often it absorbed them after converting the ruling classes. Nepal, for instance, was Buddhist until King Jayasthiti Malla decided in the fifteenth century it would be nicer to be Hindu. Traditional Nepali Buddhists stayed put since the Hindu gods were always part of Nepali Buddhism, but unable to compete in caste ranking, they have suffered socially to this day. Mongolia became Buddhist when a Tibetan adept won a religious contest; the gentle Dalai Lama was suddenly Pope to a population of rambunctious Mongols. Perhaps the smoothest mass conversion of all occurred in the year 1000 AD when the Icelandic *Althing*, the parliament, met and simply voted in Christianity for the entire country.

In one rare instance of East-West accommodation, the message of Christ may have transformed a romantic North Indian shepherd deity into the divine Krishna. Some Indian historians have noted that the earliest popularization of this long established cult began surprisingly close in time to India's first historical contact with the Christian missionary-apostle Thomas about 74 AD. This could help explain why Krishna's counsel to Arjuana in the *Bhagadvad Gita*, as a loving God incarnate as man, seems at times a South Asian Sermon on the Mount inserted into the epic war drama of the *Mahabharata*, otherwise devoted to impersonal concepts such as dharma and karma. India may have accepted the message but not the messenger. Thomas himself, according to history, was martyred on the banks of the Ganges in that year. Was martyrdom his glory, or his karma? Nobody knows. Kwan-Yin, the Chinese goddess of mercy, is often depicted with a child, an iconographic change based on Christian Madonnas introduced along the Chinese coast by Portuguese traders in the sixteenth century.

When the East rejected a religion, it was often in reaction to a foreign culture rather than a foreign theology. "First come the priests" warned the first King of Nepal, Privthi Narayan Shah, "then come the cannons." When the shoguns of sixteenth century Japan shut out Christianity, it was part of a total exclusionary policy so complete that Western technology was banned at the same time. Commodore Perry found Japanese samurai still hacking away at each other with swords in the mid-nineteenth century, hundreds of years after the development of reliable firearms.

As a result of this natural tendency to ground in a particular area, each religion in the world today is expressed and experienced through the deepest traditions of a specific regional culture. As we merge into an inevitable world consciousness during the next century, these regional beliefs may become our last links with centuries of tradition. By the 1990's, given the unsteady world conditions prevailing, it should not seem surprising that more people than ever before were discovering both the cultural security and, for many, culturally appropriate answers available through religious belief and practice.

There are two sides to this, however. In one sense we are cheered to see the Russian Patriarch again leading his flock in Moscow, the Dalai Lama meeting with leaders in religion and science, and Mother Theresa's epiphany in the slums of Calcutta. Yet in another, slightly more sinister sense, this may also represent a sort of spiritual time bomb. There's room for only so many heavens on one earth.

Can We Talk?

It would be convenient to invite Jesus Christ, Mohammed, the Buddha, Moses, Lao Tsu, Confucius, and Manu for dinner and see if they might come up with something like United Religions. Our dinner guests would probably think it was a fine idea, but since each represents a higher power, they would have to report back to God, Allah, Tao or Dharma for the go-ahead. Things might get stuck at the metaphysical level. There is good reason for this.

Western religions rely on mutually exclusive personal revelation to holy individuals such as Moses, Jesus, Mohammed, or Joseph Smith from one all-encompassing God. They have also tended to build on each other. Christianity added Jesus to Moses, Islam added Mohammed to Moses and Jesus. In America, the Mormons added Joseph Smith and

Christian Scientists in Boston lobbied for Mary Baker Eddy. Sun Myung Moon said he actually was Jesus, although followers of late Texas ex-messiah David Koresh disagreed with him. God apparently still speaks to some Westerners, including the top Mormon, but most claiming conversation with a deity these days are offered Prozac® more often than prayer.

Finding agreement among Asian believers is no easier. Most Eastern traditions replace mutually exclusive prophets of God with mutually exclusive interpretations of Dharma or Tao, the eternal universal system uniting the human physical and metaphysical experience. Hinduism is technically Sanathan Dharma, or the "traditional system." Buddha preached the Buddha Dharma, his own understanding of the way things worked. The parts are not really interchangeable. Theory and practices differ. Brahman is not Nirvana and the Tao is neither.

Getting the original sources to cooperate could be even harder. Yahweh and Allah might agree to the same menu since neither like pork, but Ram might have a beef because Hindus don't eat cows. Getting served could be dicey protocol since God wants no other gods served before Him, but it would make things simple for the Buddha since his monk's rules say to eat anything they put in his begging bowl, as long as it's in the morning. Still, once they worked out the seating they would soon discover how similar their messages were at the human level, the only level we humans could be concerned about.

Like the larger sects of a major religion, the religions of the world today all intend to lead us in the same basic directions but continue to disagree on who is to be our guide and which guidebook we are to use. The more we investigate the basic dogmas of our world religions, the more depressing it becomes. Each originates in a different land, embodies idiosyncratic traditions, and each is, to the devout, the only one there is. Furthermore, there hasn't been a really new world religion since the Sikh Dharma, Guru Nanak's alloy of Muslim and Hindu faiths. The Bahais have tried very hard, but like Esperanto, attempts at cultural amalgamation this far along lack a certain spark.

In fact, nearly all recent religious innovations have been simply new interpretations of already extant theologies. Mormons, Pentecostals, and Christian Scientists all worship the same Jesus as Roman Catholics and yet none of these sects existed two hundred years ago. The ecstatic devotion of Lord Chaitanya for Krishna in the fifteenth century originated his egalitarian Hindu sect, while the pantheism of Ramakrishna estab-lished a national following out of Victorian Calcutta. In nineteenth cen-tury Germany, Reform Judaism was born. In 20th century Japan, a Buddhist sect, Nicheren Shoshu, acquired a lay auxiliary, Sokka Gakkai, expanded, evangelized, and practiced politics until scandals separated the priesthood from the promoters.

There has been nothing radically new on the horizon for quite a long time. As it happens, the world is about due for a major religious event of some sort. In regular oscillations, periods of human pride in technology and power seem to alternate with periods of religious resurgence. The Renaissance gave impetus to the Protestants as the industrial revolution foretold the formation of the Baptists, Wesleyans, Mormons, and Methodists. Whenever it seems that mankind is becoming too arrogant with material powers, there is a social migration back to religious faith, often resulting in entirely new sects. With proliferation of so many dif-ferent religions around the globe, one can only wonder if we may be closer to new fusions than we ever expected. Like the geological pres-sures at the edge of a fault, world religious pressure is building to new intensities. The plate tectonics of regional religions is already causing eruptions all along the fault lines. This current growing worldwide shift back to stronger religious belief, especially as a force to promote national unity, might have been fine fifty years ago but the time has long passed for the promotion of any God who loves anyone especially. We are fac-ing more than a cultural shift; we may be facing a basic paradigm shift as dramatic as the notion that unbelievers could also be saints.

The Medium as the Meaning: What's Really Going On Anyway?

Nothing happens in a cultural vacuum anymore. International market-ing of everything from cigarettes to computers fuels the engines of an emerging world culture; television and the popular media expose us all to each other all the time these days. It is not the word of any God which motivates the millions, but mass marketing of images intended, ulti-mately, to sell products or politics. As advertising and personal ambition ultimately support the world media, commerce overcomes creed in the multinational marketplace. Local heroes are replaced by movie actors and international rock stars; the Saints are a pro football team from New

Orleans. The whole world delights in androgynous pop creations, MTV Madonnas, and video animations.

The unfortunate result seems to be a growing anxiety as to the source of any real truth. As psychologist Carol Moog points out in 1991, "The closer advertisers get to creating images of reality that coincide with people's perception of what reality looks like, the harder it is for consumers to test the reality of the message and dismiss it as advertising." Continually faced with censorship of information for political purposes or manipulation of information for commercial purposes, there is a growing international anxiety as to what is really going on anywhere. It is, in fact, a crisis of faith, faith that there are any real, believable answers anymore.

One overt reaction has been a growing hypersensitivity of local cultures to the invasion of global culture. Nationalism seems to be on the rise in nearly every nation. Racial, religious, and cultural violence escalate yearly as people react violently to any suggestion of shared goals and common needs. Arab nations withdraw into the Koran while religious blood feuds fuel civil war in Lebanon and Yugoslavia. Between one quarter and one half of Austrians questioned in a 1991 poll said they would not want to live next to Turks, Poles, Rumanians or Yugoslavs. Tribal violence bloodies Africa year after year; religious violence erupts in India as regularly as the monsoons.

In the United States laws are promoted establishing English as the "national language" just when more languages than ever before are being spoken from New York to Los Angeles. In a survey of 1,500 Americans by the American Jewish Committee rating attitudes for other cultures, forty percent expressed negative feelings towards "Wisians," a non-existent ethnic group added to the survey as a response gauge. Having all met each other, the concept of being adult, and responsible to forces higher than self interest, becomes increasingly unenforceable now that no one really believes that Allah is going to nuke the Jews or that Jesus saves only white Republicans. In effect, the ultimate parents have checked out, leaving us all searching for rules that we once knew by heart, and, more to the point, the mechanism of threat or reward to uphold them.

The most unsettling by-product of growing global religious pluralism has been this erosion of a believable cause-and-effect system for ethics, morality, and social behavior. This in turn has led to a rather disturbing aspect of our current world order. Everywhere we find the codifying of local culture into ever more conservative legislation, promoted by brave new alliances between religious fundamentalists and nationalistic, isolationist, and often repressive national politics. The pervasive use of local religion-based cultural "morality" as an excuse for increasing governmental control over our personal lives is at a new high. In the West, media saturation has filled the gaps with violence, making gunslinging police the enforcer gods of life and death.

In one nation after another, this regressive trend is fervently supported by local heroes claiming "traditional morality" is being threatened in a world that has lost direction and seems about to fall into a hedonistic, techno-humanitarian, sinful, Godless pluralistic chaos. In response, we make immoral illegal, and let loose the inquisition of the state against the misbehavers. Since God won't strike them down, we have to take on the job ourselves to shore up cultural habits and national mythologies with new laws, police, and prisons. Patriotism is becoming associated with the religious right in every country. Gary Bauer, President of the conservative Family Research Council, described the scene in the United States in the nineties as "an ongoing cultural civil war revolving around morality," pitting Americans "with a fairly traditional religious faith who feel that culture is out of control, against secular people who believe in a pluralistic society." In response to concerns that a free society was not going to like the idea of more legislated morality, Bauer was unconvinced. "We're pretty far away from worrying about society erring on the side of too many restrictions. The pendulum is not moving that way. Popular culture is still in the other camp."

The result has been the growing association of religion and state policy as faith and patriotism become ever more dangerously mixed. While the IRA blows up another pub for the Pope, one middle East nation after another returns to Islamic law. In China, where non-religion is the religion, the Central Committee of the Communist Party issued a twelve page directive ordering authorities to "resolutely attack counterrevolutionaries who make use of religion." In our global society, the very regionalism of the great religious faiths now provides the major irritant of social misunderstanding by promoting local homeboy fantasies of a national purpose under a national God. Opposing the notion that the earth is of common concern to us all, we are more than ever before urged to identify with simple, marketable cultural icons and ethnic symbols. For emotional outlet, national flags and colored ribbons replace personal tributes and statements.

The trend is not limited to adults. Rather than embrace the mixing of cultures on the modern university campus, students are creating ever more exclusive enclaves of their own, studying and socializing only with others like themselves. "It's just backwards," wrote educator Theodore Sizer in 1992; "We need more diversity . . . we need to train people to resist the powerful images commerce puts around us." Ernest L. Boyer, former United States Education Commissioner, agreed. "Separatism and even tribalism in the old-fashioned sense are increasing, he noted. The implications are frightening. If humanism and communal understanding cannot happen on a college campus, how in the world can it happen on city streets?"

Our sense of personal and social security, once synonymous with cultural identity and religious belief, faces ever greater challenges in today's world, a world ironically both increasingly connected and increasingly alienated. The way that local culture reacts to foreign religion has resulted in everything from violence to accommodation. Muslims face skinhead lynch mobs in Germany and Hindus endure temple "sit-ins" by immigrant Western Hare Krishnas in Nepal. The Saudi government allows no infidels into Mecca, and so to get background shots for Spike Lee's 1992 film *Malcolm X*, an entire film crew converted to Islam: mercurial Muslims at best, but Muslims none the less. Allahu Akbar!

Most of the time it is more depressing. In 1992, in Algeria, a government-backed military seized control to prevent a Muslim fundamentalist elected takeover. Egypt was nearly in similar straits and in France, politician Jean Marie LePen attracted crowds to his xenophobic, race baiting invective aimed mainly at Islamic immigrants. In the 1992 U.S. presidential elections, two out of three Republican candidates, Pat Buchanan and David Duke, campaigned on platforms that were isolationist, nationalistic, and racist at least in appearance if not in fact. Popular culture seems everywhere to be testing new levels of paranoid repression and cultural intolerance.

This could be, in other words, the appropriate catalytic time for some first attempts at new and original world religions to arise and proliferate in an increasingly interconnected, increasingly intercultural, and increasingly anxious world. To many it must seem that we are facing the apocalypse. In fact, we only need the appropriate catalyst to start a global religion on its way; some more reassuring, more universal, ethical, and above all believable faith based on wisdom we could all share equally.

High Tech Hybrids: If Ever the Time Were Ripe

With world consciousness moving from local to global concerns, typified by the worldwide ecological movement and international refugee aid, we may be about to witness a global "faithquake" resulting ultimately in completely new religions based more on global understanding than local traditions. Rather than avoiding science, it seems probable that any new religious philosophies will embrace technology as a tool for discovery and compassion rather than simply the cutting edge for business or for war.

So far, at least in this century, the major role of technology in the service of religion has been to increase the reach of already established world faiths. There has been no United Nations "Religion Project" to coordinate the theologians, psychologists, philosophers and phenomenologists. The closest contender for a sect with a high-tech terminology would be L. Ron Hubbard's neo-rationalist Scientology, but despite the apparent utility of some of its simpler auto-hypnotic practices, it lacks a comprehensive philosophical and ethical structure and cannot, therefore, attract broad social support.

Even more interesting mutants have arisen from the adoption of techno-jargon by promoters of seminars based on original mindscience philosophies from EST to Neuro-Linguistic Programming, each claiming a "scientific" basis. In precisely the manner that medieval mountebanks adapted "hocus pocus" from the priest's *hoc est corpus Christi,* "this is the body of Christ," creating a pseudo-Latin incantation to mislead village oafs, scientific sounding philosophies are usually more convincing to seekers functionally illiterate in the very sciences they cite to buttress their beliefs.

It is a shame that nothing resembling a global faith has sprung up anywhere recently given the current circumstances. With satellite, phone, and fax our global net is already beginning to shrink us into an interconnected people separated only incidentally by geography and culture. Cultures and practices are blending as never before. In Malaysia recently, for example, high school education was offered in Chinese, Malay, and English. The number of students in each category were roughly equal until parents began to discover that good English was worth more in the job market. More parents began sending their children to English schools. This in turn began breaking down traditional barriers between local ethnic Chinese minorities whose children now shared English as a common tongue. All over the world it is happening.

And it has happened before. The rapid spread of early Christianity was due largely to the existence of Greek communities in numerous cities lining the perimeter of the Mediterranean Sea. The Roman empire, nearly at its historic height, interconnected the entire Greco-Roman world in a common law and language. The message of Jesus, carried from city to city by the journeys of Paul and other early apostles, found a receptive audience mainly among Hellenic Romans and Greeks adrift without a religion that made any sense and too many philosophies that did.

If there were ever a time similar to the Roman empire at the birth of the Christian era, when a faith could travel nearly everywhere that counted in a short time, we have nearly identical conditions now with our interlinked global communications networks. In our current scenario, the globe becomes the Mediterranean, and the plight of the early pre-Christians is at hand. They had all the Greek religions and the Roman religions and some Egyptian cults on the side. Those disliking the devotional ceremonies of the Mithraic mysteries often found doctrinaire Stoics a bit too Zen. Intellectuals rarely believed in Zeus, but criticized the Epicureans as "be here now" utopians of doubtful patriotism. To many Greeks, Judaism was appealing, but ritual circumcision was appalling. Still, many were attracted to its monotheism and sense of social justice.

The messianic promise of Christianity, combined with the full richness of its Jewish heritage, was different and exciting. Once St. Paul pioneered baptism without circumcision, a crucial turning point in the faith, the Christian message spread from one Greek community to another. Every book in the New Testament was written in Greek, the common scientific and philosophical language of the Roman empire. Jesus, who spoke Aramaic, could not have read his own Gospels. His message was, surprisingly, more relevant to a people he had never known than to his Jewish co-religionists. The time was right, society was ripe for a change; and in less than a hundred years the Gospel had spread everywhere Latin or Greek was spoken. In three hundred years Christianity was the religion of the Western world.

In a similar vein the present world provides us with more than a dozen major world faiths, each with scores of legitimate variations not to mention general philosophical schools, cultural traditions, and regional cults led by local charismatics from swamis to Swaggarts. There is no end to the choices available these days, from the God of Abraham to the Gods of Zoroaster. There is one vast difference, however, and it is in the power which organized religion actually holds in modern secular society. One of the more useful results of the intercultural blending among the nations of the world is an agreement on rule by law rather than by dictate. Since human law is traditionally enforced by secular authority, in the 20th century traditional values are increasingly promoted by civil, rather than religious agencies from the Red Cross to the Girl Scouts. Ironically, the most brutal behavior seems to originate with those claiming to be guided by a fundamental religious belief. The last decade of the twentieth century has been, in this respect, rather grim.

In the past dozen years we have watched fundamentalist Muslims in Iran kill Bahais, fundamentalist Hindus in Bombay kill Muslims, Buddhist Sri Lankans kill Hindu Tamils, Communist Cambodians kill Buddhist Cambodians, Christian Americans kill Iraqi Muslims, and God or Allah or Jehovah is behind all this? Not bloody likely, but try to convince a fundamentalist of any major faith that the unbeliever may also go to heaven and some holy quote will be produced proving otherwise. There is only so much flexibility available if one has to ultimately ground in religious dogma.

In 1991, at the World Council of Churches meeting in Canberra, Australia, a Greek Orthodox prelate protested that Korean feminist theologian Chung Hyun-Kyung's depiction of the Buddhist "bodhisattva of compassion," Kwan-yin, or Kanon, as an image of the Holy Spirit had gone too far. An invocation which included elements of native American appeals to the forces of nature was similarly criticized as being nearly pagan. As our world culture grows, it is increasingly difficult to be a religious purist, and in response, the purists insist even more upon getting back to fundamentals. By 1993, this trend had become so potentially divisive that Pope John Paul II felt called upon to urge American bishops to combat a "bitter, ideological" feminism among some American Catholic women which he identified with "forms of nature worship and celebration of myths and symbols."

This is, in essence, the basis of the underlying problem. All attempts at world ecumenism have been unsuccessful from the start because they always started from the basis of one major world faith or another. A broad minded Buddhist cannot really be a Christian any more than a sincere Muslim could embrace Judaism. A religious person has to be a this or a that. Less religious individuals have an even greater problem. To define one's self as agnostic or atheist seems to express an active nihilism that few actually feel. Indeed, many of those who are lukewarm about their faith would enjoy a deeper devotion, but do not know how to find it without submerging their intellect in the passivity of dogma and ritual.

A Scientific Approach?

The challenge facing any emerging new world "faith" is that it cannot be in opposition to any other. It must come from an entirely new direction. It would be impossible for a new world religion to supplant or absorb any major world faith; there are simply too many of the faithful. There could arise, however, higher order philosophies based on generally accepted knowledge, knowledge not available in the past. Such revelation would not require a holy book of rules and religious history, nor a social philosophy set down by an anointed one and his followers in ancient times. If these premises were accepted as culturally transparent, they need not conflict with religious faith.

The most universally believable higher force for the past five centuries has not been religion, but science; arguably the most powerful religion on the planet today. Imagine using scientific method to provide answers as unequivocal as religions do, articulate a comprehensive philosophy of life, justify a moral code, and provide inspirational practices for personal self improvement. Much of the above has, in fact, been worked out in theory and sometimes in practice. What seems to have been lacking is the articulation of a comprehensive philosophical structure that could tie together reality, as we experience it, into some meaningful pattern. The Roman Catholic catechism asks "What is the purpose of man" and provides an answer. Until recently when it came to questions such as those, science drew a blank and religion stepped in. Many of the major questions that trouble us, we are told, are not scientifically answerable. These are, unfortunately, some of the real head-scratchers of human life.

What makes it even more difficult is that answers provided by religious texts tend to operate within an eternal system that seems at odds with the laws of time and space. Science is here to define and manipulate temporal laws, but the holy books discuss eternal truths and concepts such as the life, or the lives, everlasting. If science located an everlasting anything it would be difficult to describe. It could not publish definitive results until after the end of forever, which sums up the situation. When compared against each other, science and religion often tend to make the other seem trivial in the most fundamental enterprises of human life. Who has the answers?

Does natural law exist by the will of God? Is there an ultimate reality that centers us universally and personally, that pertains to our enemy just as us, that sets the limits of our existence in a manner we can intuit, for reasons which seem just? Is there a reason to be good? More to the point, is there any way we can find that point of reference that will allow us to answer these questions without offending either the rational or the faithful?

2

The Metaphysics of Neuroscience

Paradigms for Consciousness

"To study metaphysics as they have been studied appears to me to be like puzzling at astronomy without mechanics. . . We must bring some <u>stable</u> *foundation to argue from."*

— *Charles Darwin*

The world desperately needs a basis for faith that is universally accept-able. The central role of regionally-based religions in worldwide ethnic and social strife strongly suggests that if we could put this all behind us, we could move to something better. Each year we are moving closer to a common world currency; are we also moving towards a globalization of what we now call religion?

It would make things much easier if our respected religious leaders could come to some sort of general agreement on not only what consti-tutes naughty and nice, but why, and not just because their particular scriptures say so. In a world of over six billion humans, we ought to have enough accumulated experience to derive some general guidelines for good human behavior that transcend local tradition and national poli-tics.

The real problem, in fact, has very little to do with this sort of wisdom. Nobody really disagrees about naughty and nice. It's not even a matter of cultures; sushi is all over America and McDonalds are all over the world. Religion is much more than theology, the philosophical structure

that answers the eternal questions. Basically, every religion on earth today that enjoys credibility, cultural acceptance and at least a half million
followers is defined by three general areas of thought and practice. The
first could be termed "Cultural Ceremonies." The second would be
"Applied Social Psychology." The smallest area is "Metaphysics," the
theology or philosophy behind it all.

Looking at it realistically, the greater part of most religious activity in
any part of the world today is taken up by the first two categories. Our
cultural calendars are dotted with regional, national, and even international observances of religious rites and holidays. Christmas is a world
event celebrated in Bombay and Tokyo and Muslims shuttle to Mecca
from Morocco, Marseilles, and Memphis, Tennessee. Everyone has
New Year's parties, saints' days, and local celebrations. If it doesn't disrupt the local social fabric, nearly any form of personal religious obser-
vance is respected. Cultural politics may clash, as in Ireland and India,
but as individuals we have no quarrel with another's yearly cycle of faith
and celebration provided they stay within the cultural expectations of our
region.

A second area of religious practice, "Applied Social Psychology," is
even less of a problem. This is because the great lawgivers gained their
followings because they had the vision to perceive the universalities of
human social behavior, the ability to break it down into simple rules, and
the charisma to convince others to use these rules as a basis for personal
and social guidance. Any savior too specific for general acceptance ends
up with a cult, not a cathedral. Mother Anne Lee's Shakers are gone.
There are no Essenes in Judea nor Kadam-pas in Tibet and we could fit
all remaining Swedenborgians in a large auditorium. Twice as many met
at Woodstock in '69 as practiced Christian Science in 1994.

Tolerance of another's religious customs becomes a necessary fact of
life when so many traditions mingle in the crossroads of our growing
global society. We can't convert them all, and those religions which get
pushy about specifics will simply lose out. Most at risk are those which
require an actual hereditary link for membership. This trend is especially
pernicious to religions that do not accept conversion. Orthodox Hindus
and Jews alike watch their numbers shrink as a percentage each generation. Orthodox Parsees, who require both parents to be Parsees, are an
endangered species. Descended from the original Zoroastrians, they represent the oldest continually practiced organized religion on earth. Less

than a hundred thousand survive and there's nothing any non-Parsee can do about it. Even the world's largest organized religion, the Roman Catholic Church, is fighting for its intellectual survival as ancient customs limit a branch of Christianity interpreted by a celibate male priesthood. In the United States, "lapsed Catholics," as a group, are the single largest denomination, by numbers, in the entire country.

Only theologies based on a clear philosophical grasp of human nature, expressed in a manner universal enough for translation and adaptation, can hope to last more than a few generations. This is why the Hindu Shiv Sena movement in India is as doomed as the Christian Science Church; neither will survive the 21st century. The former is too violent to be considered truly Hindu; the latter too identified with the teachings of Mrs. Eddy, a Victorian charismatic. Any rules for human life and living, at the heart of all world religions, must be very broadly based.

At this broader level of human behavior nobody has any serious differences. Allah demands generosity, Jesus preaches humility, Moses and Buddha remind us not to kill, and Krishna asks us to open our hearts to devotion and love. All advise us to help the weak, support the poor, heal the sick, and be honest with each other. Their rationales differ, but the results are the same. Most Hindus in Calcutta revere Mother Theresa, and the Dalai Lama won the Nobel Peace Prize. Goodness is recognized everywhere, kindness is always welcome and love embraced as a human response to the tragic beauty of life. Seen in this way, all religions mirror an inherent human wisdom that seems universal in nature and specific in the telling. We have no unbelievers here either, nor any reason to disagree.

Between the celebrations and proper behavior, two thirds of our religious faith and practice is nearly convertible from one cultural currency to another. Despite the apparent differences between a Jew and a Muslim or between a Hindu and a Catholic, we seem to agree on almost all the day to day questions of real life and how we are to behave towards each other. We would enjoy most of each other's parties and ceremonies too. So what remains to quibble about?

The only area in which religions really differ is in the third category, metaphysics. Metaphysics are those areas that tend to transcend accepted limits of rational inquiry. Bertrand Russell, the celebrated mathematician and agnostic, once made up a list of five questions he claimed science was unable to answer: "Is there survival after death?", "Does mind dominate matter or vice versa?", "Is there a purpose to the universe?", "Is there validity in the assumption of natural law?", and "What is the importance of life in the cosmic scheme?" Only God or Dharma, we are told, have the clues to those ones, and only individuals made acceptable by ritual initiation, rites, and specialized education are entrusted with the interpretation. Unfortunately, they all seem to differ. It's not the eternal questions that keep us apart so much as the variety we find in the answers. That this nearly academic aspect of religious practice was the basis of so much suffering in the twentieth century will be the source of wonder in the twenty-first. Still, at this time, most religions continue to insist their specific answers are the one and only truth despite how unlikely they may seem to others.

There is another possibility shaping up, however, which seems to have passed unnoticed. Since all major religions are adaptable, they must be somewhat pliable. Nearly all religious dogma is based on interpretations of statements or writings general enough to transcend culture. New interpretations are never unthinkable. Returning to the "faithquake" metaphor, just as pressure at the earth's core can make even solid rock flow like plastic, so contemporary social pressures might become intense enough to force new adaptations and interpretations of the most traditional and accepted main line faiths.

If we could find a basis for a shared metaphysics, we might finally learn to appreciate our global religions for what they are, poetic wisdom from our personal ancestors who needed no positron emission tomagraphs or scanning electron microscopes to perceive the underlying wisdom of human existence. Wisdom is found in the universals, not the details, and a universal human metaphysics could be possible only if the details had no cultural basis or bias at all. There seems only one way to do this.

The Metaphysics of Neuroscience

Scoping out new answers to unanswerable questions would seem beyond the scope of one person or even a group of specialists. The wreckage of countless attempts to come up with explanations and schemas litter the shelves of the book stores. At this time, the greatest amount of interest seems to be focused on the area of the mind sciences and recent investigations into the general phenomenon we call consciousness.

There is a good reason for this. No matter what faith we follow, we are by now all aware that there are millions of people who believe otherwise and seem not only to survive, but to prosper. The ability to accept that there are a lot of different religions without making further judgments as to which is right or wrong can lead to a simple line of reasoning: All human cultures seem to have religions. Therefore, the basis of all human religions might well be found within the nature of consciousness itself.

In other words, observing groups of humans in different areas over time, they will always find religion of one kind or another even if they may disagree in the details. If this is the case, it would strongly suggest that the source of religious faith may be internally generated. It could be a species-wide need-to-know externalized through varying, but remarkably similar, social structures, customs, and belief systems wherever human culture has reached a certain level of development. This line of thinking could, in turn, lead one step further: anything common to human consciousness would have to be the result of something at a neurological level, something in the way the brain works, which ends up affecting all humans in a similar way, and which is then expressed differently in different cultures.

This is probably the path to follow, although it is initially distasteful for the uninitiated. The dualism of Descartes, suggesting a mechanistic brain that fabricates the mind, gives Hindus hives and Christians the creeps. Seeking clues to the spirit or the soul in a mass of wires and plumbing puts off both Baptists and Buddhists alike. Still, it remains the most likely direct route to the root of religious experience as we perceive it. The brain is, after all, the only organ capable of conscious perception. We can't do it with our toes or our tonsils.

This is nothing very recent. The primary importance of the brain in the perception of consciousness in all its forms has been well known since the ancients. Most of the methods by which the brain accomplishes this task, on the other hand, have only recently been revealed to us through computerized medical technology. The proliferation of linkages between brain science and computer science has nurtured a powerful alliance during the last twenty years. The architecture of the brain is finally being defined, and it is beginning to provide us with the first clues to the language of the mind itself. In fact, it becomes ever more likely that philosophers or theologians of the twenty first century will be required to show fluency in mind science just as modern medical doctors must know their biochemistry. Things have changed that much in the last twenty five years.

As a natural result, we are drawing closer to new philosophical structures which might finally harmonize scientific method and religious belief. The absolutely correct term for this would have to be the cumbersome "neurophenomenology," literally "using the neurological sciences to determine the nature of reality," and this is, in fact, what seems to be emerging. "Neurotheology" has two less syllables, says basically the same thing, and links it specifically to religious philosophies. Just as Thomas Aquinas developed his philosophical system, Thomism, utilizing Aristotelian logic to order and anchor Christian theology, so modern religious thinkers are starting to use the structures of brain science to provide intellectually universal and generally agreeable points on which to base their conclusions.

One of the best reasons to use brain science as the basis for a comprehensive systematic phenomenology is the simple reductionist argument that since we only experience what we perceive, we had best first study the structure and function of our major organ of perception. In learning more about the way we perceive reality itself, we may discover clues leading to simple and believable explanations of otherwise traditionally unexplainable mysteries. There are limits to our understanding, but this may be much more because of the way the brain arranges consciousness than any lack of enlightenment, devotion, or grace.

Virtual Religion?

The concept of consciousness as the result of a biochemical system is just the sort of systematic viewpoint which seems to be rapidly overtaking the world. From the ecology of the earth to the networking of databases, systematic perspectives seem to be emerging in many areas. Still, would we be willing to give up individual saviors and prophets for a better system, even if it preserved the beauty and the wisdom of our ancient religious heritage? We have accepted our beliefs as reality; could we reweave that fabric with a common thread and still be as sure?

If the rules of consciousness turn out to be flexible under some circumstances, given the proper conditions might we perceive a timeless eternity or have a transcendental experience? The philosophical implications of recent research along this line of speculation, taken far enough, are already suggesting there are answers to most of Russell's questions. In the process of normal brain death, for instance, we will all experience states of consciousness in which the perception of both time and space are greatly altered. The real problem is that if we use brain science to answer the question "What really happens when we die?" and such a theory became generally accepted, every religion on earth would have to either deny it or demonstrate that their holy scriptures could include it by flexible interpretation of dogma.

In fact, as some of these theories were being worked out, there was for a time serious apprehension that any genuine breakthrough in this delicate area could create volatile, perhaps even violent, reactions among devout followers of one religion or another. Copernicus waited nearly until his death to publish, and at this writing, Salman Rushdie is still in hiding. People get very emotional about their religious beliefs. Going to heaven without believing in Jesus is impossible for a Baptist and any suggestion to the contrary is heretical. If eternity were found to be a state of mind experienced during brain death, any sinner might deny his Christ and theoretically, if not theologically, make it home free. Belief is belief, and if a concept appears valid enough that it becomes widely accepted, the believer is as assured of heaven by that means as any other. Would neurological answers be inherent heresy, repugnant to the sincerely religious of every faith?

There are, it turns out, few scriptural bars to contemporary explanations so long as they do not deny the event. Finding the bones of Jesus Christ would be cataclysmic, proving His existence to the unbeliever while also denying His ascension, a basic item of Christian doctrine. Such a discovery would forever be contested and the discoverer marked for life as the source of a serious schism in the faith. One cannot deny basic dogma and hope to escape censure. Fortunately, finding a scientific explanation for the experience of an eternal afterlife does not deny the event. It should, after all, be within the power of God or the Dharma to design us in such a way that we might transcend properly to our heavens without smoke and mirrors.

In Benares, for instance, many Hindus believe that Bhairab, the lord of death, allows those fortunate enough to die within the sacred city to avoid the tedious rounds of rebirth by simply collapsing their future lives into one amazing instant so that they can "see Shiva" immediately. This endless lifetime express has never been investigated, but insights into how Bhairab might accomplish his feat do not invalidate the event. Describing the method need not reject the miraculous. It can even reinforce and revitalize the faithful to realize that the divine beauty they can see in a sunset cannot in any way be diminished by a basic understanding of the biochemistry of its earthly perception.

Historically, religion is usually accommodating. Only a few preachers had serious problems with Charles Darwin's theories. A more typical Victorian clergyman, Charles Kingsley, read the recently published *Origin of Species* and wrote to the author, "I have gradually learnt to see that it is just as noble a conception of Deity, to believe He created primal forms capable of self development into all forms needful *pro tempore* and *pro loco*, as to believe that He required a fresh act of intervention to supply the *lacunae* which He Himself had made. I question whether the former be not the loftier thought."

Darwin's theory, like that of Copernicus, simply provided a better system to explain fundamental aspects of the nature of the world around us. It did, however, trigger a basic restructuring of scientific thought similar to that which followed the work of Copernicus. These radical changes in perspective were identified and described by philosopher Thomas Kuhn as "paradigm shifts." In a paradigm shift, a new perspective forces restructuring of the predominant viewpoint, such as the shift from the geocentric Ptolemaic astronomy to the Copernican heliocentric system.

The "Copernican Revolution" was a fundamental philosophical event. Once man was no longer the center of the universe, all sorts of other assumptions began to cave in. Religion has always had a connection with natural science, and by the sixteenth century Christian theology had embraced Ptolemaic astronomy. The concentric spheres of the Ptolemaic universe seemed a bit lonely, and so medieval Christian writers populated them with all manner of heavenly winged creatures. Having deeded the heavenly spheres to cherubim, seraphim, archangels, and so on, it was embarrassing to evict them all. For a time it seemed easier to evict the Copernicans, but too many telescopes confirmed the results.

As paradigm shifts are not improvements in the old system but the unexpected introduction of a new system, they inevitably face opposition from the many institutions and individuals who are associated in one way or another with the status quo. There were many universities at the time of Copernicus, and professors of Ptolemaic astronomy were the only ones available. Some switched over easily, others were dragged kicking and fussing into the new era. Some never do switch. The great Victorian scientist and explorer Louis Agassiz discovered the ice age and collected many fossils, but he never accepted Darwinian evolution.

Even when science has shifted, it can take centuries for a cultural interpretation to change worldwide. By 1991 nearly all educated scientists accepted the evolution of species, but 47% of Americans responding to a Gallup poll that year still believed that God created man "pretty much in his present form at one time within the last 10,000 years." Basic breakthroughs in science and philosophy can take time to earn wide popular acceptance.

Werner Heisenberg meets William of Ockham

Paradigm shifts are always characterized by two qualities. They seem nearly obvious once described, and yet they always required the best science of the time to provide the information which made the new perspective possible. When the new insight finally occurs, it often happens so dramatically that it seems sudden and unexpected even to the discoverer, although it is nearly always the result of many years of effort. "At first I was deeply alarmed," wrote Werner Heisenberg, describing his initial insight into quantum mechanics. "I had the feeling that, through the surface of atomic phenomena, I was looking at a strangely beautiful interior, and felt almost giddy at the thought that now I had to probe this wealth of mathematical structures nature had so generously spread before me. I was far too excited to sleep."

Others report the same experience: the alarming discovery of a new way of understanding some basic phenomena, profound in implication and yet so elegant in concept that it simply must be right. The new theory itself often proliferates so fast that it takes time for the proof to catch up to it. The Copernican system, as it was first published, was faulty. It required the combined work of Johannes Kepler, Tyco Brahe and Isaac Newton to both prove and improve a system so obvious it was already widely accepted. Copernicus had utilized the best observations late Renaissance technology had to offer. It was enough on which to base a theory more elegant than the technology itself could adequately support. It was likewise not discovered until the 20th century that Isaac Newton had fudged some of the experiments he described in the proofs of his *Principia*. The structure was so elegant that he would not let the limitations of his own instruments, far too crude to yield such accuracy, get in the way of his new discovery. It made too much sense to be wrong, so he ran with it even when he knew he might never be able to prove it.

The elegance of the ideas which re-order the thinking of an era always reflect an inherent simplicity. In this, they all tend to conform to the ex- ample of Ockham's razor, a philosophical observation by the 14th cen- tury English cleric William of Ockham. His insight, proven again and again throughout the history of science, is expressed most simply by the phrase "nature abhors complexity." In other words, given two possible explanations for any phenomena, the simpler is invariably correct. The theories of Nicholas Copernicus, Isaac Newton, Charles Darwin, Albert Einstein, Niels Bohr, Werner Heisenberg and Stephen Hawking all ex- plain a wider range of physical phenomena with a more compact system than had been previously available. Each of these new perspectives al- lowed new and unexpected observations to fit into a radically different, but inherently simple, structure.

It is the second aspect of paradigm shifts that may not be as immedi- ately apparent to a purely philosophical investigation. It seems the theo- ries that change the way we think are nearly all catalyzed by very specific advances in technology Without the improved mechanics of the Renaissance, the lenses of Anton Leuwenhoek would not have been there for Galileo or for Newton. Without the improvements of Newtonian physics, there could not have been a nineteenth century Michaelson- Morely speed of light experiment to provide the new questions that Einstein finally answered. Like relay runners passing the baton, finer science creates finer theory, which in turn creates even finer science. It was only a matter of time before the tools of brain science would provide the perspective with which such a paradigm shift would be possible if not inevitable. A new perspective is now emerging, as radically different from the traditional world view as the solar system of Copernicus was from Ptolemy.

The Neurotheological Paradigm

Our sense of reality is generally accepted to be a reaction to what ac- tually is. We are taught that the manner of this reaction determines a lot about our evaluation of a person's mental state. The world is real, but we interpret it differently; the universe is relatively fixed in time and space and the way we interact with it is the variable. This is the way current philosophy works. From the neurotheological viewpoint, this is backwards. The only place to start is to begin by acknowledging that the reality we perceive at any time is a virtual reality, perceived by a consciousness with rules and limits determined by what is available, neurologically speaking, to work with in any given brain at any given moment. Reality is not decreed, it is perceived, and it can be deceived as well in ways we can understand, predict, and ultimately influence during our lives.

If the world we perceive and believe in is a virtual reality, a product of a process, then as that process undergoes predictable distortions, such as in extreme stress or the progressive stages of brain death, might we not then find ourselves in another universe entirely, as real to us, and just as believable, as the one we now perceive? Is this what happens? This is just one example of a new exploration which combines elements of religion, developmental psychology, and developmental neurology. It opens the door on a new perspective, one which may forever change the way many people think about the way they think, know, feel, and even believe.

3

Virtually Real

Painting By Numbers

*"One ought to know that on the one hand plea-
sure, joy, laughter, and games, and on the other
grief, sorrow, discontent and dissatisfaction
arise only from the brain. It is especially by it
that we think, comprehend, distinguish the ugly
from the beautiful, the bad from the good, the
agreeable from the disagreeable..."*

— Hippocrates

Reality, Perception, and Appearance

Our perception of the world around us and our thoughts about that
world take place in the brain at the same time. There is a real difference,
however, between the world we perceive and the world that really is. For
example, it requires 200 quadrillionths of a second for a rhodopsin
molecule in the retina to swivel in place when it is energized by the impact of a single photon of light. This momentary structural change in that
one molecule initiates a complex series of interconnected events which
eventually create our sense of sight. This is where it all starts.

The photon is travelling, naturally, at the speed of light, but once it hits
the rhodopsin, things start bogging down at the very first quadrillionth.
Who knows, in other words, what's happened between the time the photon hits and the time we can even begin the process of seeing it? In some
sub-atomic worlds a lot can happen in two hundred quads. What this
means is that at any time we are seeing a world that is slightly behind
"real time." We perceive a scene that took place at some previous time.
Any reality we can see or perceive must then be a representation, a per-

ception to which we react and relate with. It can be no more than a "virtual reality." It can't be real, but we think it is.

Our moment-to-moment reality is seamless, virtual because we can't perceive the full synthesis of perception. Even if we could, we could not change it and there would be no reason to do so. Still, as all our perceptions must be generated out of a pattern of pulses travelling through neuronal networks, any reality we can perceive must be a "virtual reality." It must occur within a number of typical limitations peculiar to our biological systems, just as a computer-generated virtual reality operates within the rule structures of a computer environment.

The term virtual reality, in computer language, describes the reality perceived within a computer-generated environment. At this time, computer programs which can create interactive visual environments have progressed to the point at which one can "walk through" models created by complex programs, even modifying scenery and structures by adding doors, windows, and walls at will.   Cutting-edge cyberpunk entrepreneurs are already promoting a brave new dimension in entertainment. Customers don stereo vision micro-monitor helmets, put on a pair of interactive gloves, clip on body-movement sensors, and are projected right into the scene they are watching. For a dollar a minute they can actually "be" Super Mario, an interactive part of the ultimate computer game. A U.S. Defense Department DARPA project went one further, creating complete databases by obtaining interviews with every single participant of certain Persian Gulf battles. The result is interactive group-gropes involving dozens of trainees in video helmets blasting their way through not-real encounters of the virtual kind. It seems to train them just as well, and it saves a lot of ammunition.

Needless to say, aside from the DARPA level toys, these "virtual realities" are a lot less than believable, and it takes about six million gigabits worth of memory to generate the constantly shifting scenes. The concept has been exploited beyond all technological boundaries in Hollywood films such as *Lawnmower Man, Toys*, and the 1993 television series *Wild Palms*. Still, bearing in mind similar rapid advancements in other areas of computer science, it would not be unreasonable to expect that within a dozen years or so we could enter a booth, activate a wrap-around screen, put on a pair of transducer gloves, sink into a senso-lounger, and find ourselves in a jungle, a beach, or the surface of the moon. For a dollar a minute we could live in a "virtual reality" battling tigers or romancing a movie star.

There are clearly a number of levels of "realities" at work in such a scenario. The first level is the only one the player can, and should, perceive. Supposing, though, that the player were a programmer. She might know that her virtual Tom Cruise could say lovely things but he could not hum. He could sing and harmonize with the player, perhaps, but only in major and minor keys. The rare Bengali lass who wanted to sing a raga with virtual Tom would be mildly disappointed.

However, there is a deeper reality which organizes the Tom Cruise program itself: the computer language, or "platform" on which it is based. Is Tom in UNIX or MS-DOS? Maybe they wrote it in ADA or PASCAL or a language just called "C." "C" has rules, just as there are rules to UNIX and MS-DOS, which limit and structure the environment in which the program operates. If a player, slashing his way through a virtual jungle, were expert in UNIX, he might at one point wonder in what language the program was written, but he would have no way to determine the answer unless he saw the program itself.

Underlying the computer language itself is the computer's own virtual reality, the microcode. The basic computational environment of a digital computer is a binary reality, a quantum world of zeroes and ones, the search for signal versus "noise," the "there" or "not there" of minute electrical pulses travelling at the speed of light through the murky chaotic static of an electromagnetic universe. No matter how complex the command or the program instruction, it is ultimately read by the computer as a series of ones and zeros. However, the quantum leaps from 001001100111, or "multiply value in memory location x by 2 and store in location y" to the wisps of fractal clouds drifting in front of the virtual moon on Tom's binary beach are just too far removed for any meaningful correspondence. So the programmer asks virtual Tom to kiss her, and naturally he does.

Finally, there are ultimate physical limitations in the nature of all digital computers which underlie everything else. A value is either zero or it is one; there is no one-half, or "maybe." There must be electricity and some form of memory. The silicon, metal, and plastic environment cannot be baked, burnt, broken, steamed, shocked, or boiled. If anything like that happens, the computer simply won't work at all, and probably won't ever again. Goodbye Tom, goodbye beach.

This illustration describes a hierarchy of interdependent, ever more sophisticated, invisible physical rules and logical systems that limit all forms of virtual perception. This nesting of systems within systems to create "reality" is about as close to the real meaning of the Sanskrit word "dharma" as we could wish for. There is no reality except a perception which in itself depends on a system. There is no God in virtual Tom's world; everything is within the system which starts with a one or a zero. A similar series of hierarchies is at work within our human brain at any time, structuring a vast interconnected biological environment, the unimaginably complex system required for the perception of human consciousness. By observing the biological systems behind the perception of our consciousness, we may begin to determine, if nothing else, some basic rules behind all the other rules.

The ground rules of our consciousness are simple and absolutely quantifiable. Our brain requires 3.3 ml. of oxygen for every 100 grams of mass per minute and a blood glucose level of 80-120 mg. per 100 ml. It must eliminate waste toxins, which also requires a rich circulatory system. Every little part of it has precise requirements and limitations. The brain can't survive ten minutes without oxygen; any single blood vessel can clog or rupture for any reason and irreparable parts could be gone forever in five minutes. We might never speak again. Within two hours a glucose failure can be fatal, a threat too well known to diabetics. Anything that interrupts the blood flow will stop everything. The result is always coma followed by death. These are basic operating rules that cannot be altered; nobody has ever recovered from brain death. There are some other limitations, however, which are not so obvious.

Warps in the Enchanted Weave

The brilliant neurologist Charles Sherrington once referred to the brain as the "enchanted loom," as it seemed to create without effort the seamless tapestry of our mental experience. We have progressed beyond learning the basic needs of the brain by now; we have reached the point where we can begin to describe both how the loom works . . . and how it doesn't work quite so well in some cases.

Many insights gained in this way have but limited use. It is true that we cannot see in the ultra violet spectrum or hear much above twenty kilohertz, but these are not the limitations that affect us. The unheard and the unseen have little effect on everyday life. At a more basic level, however, nobody is suggesting that the brain is operating with anything but neurons. Whatever consciousness is, we perceive it with nerve cells and not muscle fibers. We also know that these nerve cells, when excited biochemically, "fire" minute electrical pulses. By this means information is relayed from cell to cell during normal brain activity. We know this; it is not a theological point or a philosophical conjecture. It is a known fact.

Since the electrochemical pulse from an activated brain cell is the equivalent of "1," while the latency period without a pulse is the equivalent of a "0," the most basic underlying operating imperative of our perception would be the ability to sense the difference between the two. Consciousness seems to arise from a sophisticated form of chaotic pattern recognition, and a pattern can only be defined by the use of contrast. To that extent, brain cells and computer chips share a common reliance on comparative functions to get the computational job done, the same signal-to-noise ratio, pulse or no-pulse, dot or dash, "there" or "not there." A neuron that couldn't tell the difference would be as useless as a binary circuit that didn't know zero from one.

At the surface level of our awareness this most basic functional operative is nearly completely invisible; it does not affect the colors of the day or the thoughts of our mind. Only if we try to think about something that a pulse-based consciousness cannot think about do we get into any trouble. Usually, when we try to do this it's either difficult or disturbing, almost as if there were something wrong with our mental focus button. Try, for example, to picture "forever." Non-comparatives just won't compute in a comparative cognitive environment. We know what the word means, but we can't make a mental picture or find words for abstracts as we can for images we acquire from experience.

Forever is just one example. Human consciousness is perceived through neural communications in which everything depends on the presence or absence of voltage potentials. Since our method of cognition is comparison, we can't communicate about any non-comparable states at all. We can't really describe "perfect" any better than we can paint "never"; it's a problem with information being passed around in a comparative form. This is not to say that we cannot have experiences or feelings in which such states are momentarily certainly present; just that we cannot use standard cognitive reflective thought to describe or articulate them.

In fact, events in which such non-comparative experiences take place are usually highly charged emotional personal or religious experiences during which nobody would be likely to suggest that cognitive reflective thought was being used. Our hormonally-driven emotional feelings resemble wave phenomena closer to analog events while communication and cognition tend toward the digital. Our neural electrochemistry embraces both levels but we "think" in ways we can discuss with other people and "experience" those non-comparative states that we cannot ever really communicate in a rational or cognitive manner.

Perhaps, then, we cannot know the nature of God simply because neuron-based brains can't handle the infinite, per se, at all? From a cost accountant's point of view, this makes very good evolutionary sense as we don't encounter that many incomparable beings in our lifetimes. This could be one good reason why it has been so difficult to communicate with the Divine, or at least why it might be hard for humans. It seems that the incomparable can happen but it doesn't compute, just as we can "know" and "experience" things we can't think about or describe in words.

This is but one example of the perspective required if we are going to interrelate the truth of science and the truth of religion. There is no scientific problem with saying "The perfection of God is hidden from the understanding of man" because, neurologically speaking, the human brain can't really mentally image a "perfect" state whatever it is. It is an inherent built-in design limitation of our neural method of perceiving consciousness and we wouldn't be humans without it.

Maybe God made us that way? Who knows? It doesn't really much matter. We are interacting with a chaotic world every day and it's a blessing that consciousness does as well as it does even if we can't see ultra-violet or describe the transcendental.

This sort of viewpoint provides a space for both the experience of the divine from a personal point of view for those who have had such experiences and cannot deny them, and for a scientific, rational explanation as well. God alone could divine the basis and method of divine perception. The basis of human perception remains locked into the neuron-dharma, the systems within systems of brain cells that pulse or don't pulse, require sugar and oxygen to survive, and cannot be damaged or starved or they will die and, incidentally, take us with them.

Time and Space Taffy

At the most basic level we know that all human conscious perception is possible only through neurological systems in a delicately balanced biochemical environment. This perspective on the nature of consciousness goes much further than detailing the biological limits of the human brain. Extrapolated into either religion or science, it is equally obtrusive in both camps. On one hand it may dim the attraction of seeking perfection to realize that we can't describe it in any detail using the human mental system. Clearly, if nobody can adequately describe it, we certainly couldn't tell anyone what to look for. It seems we may have to "know" it when and if we find it because it may exist only in the realm of experience, unrecognizable to anyone but ourselves and dependent on the time in our life as well as the space we were in at the given moment. Science fares no better.

Norman Ramsey, who won the Nobel Prize in physics for developing the atomic clock, points out time is measured by periodicity. From sunrise and seasons to the picosecond beats of vibrating cesium atoms, it is the regular repetition of something that sets the foundation for the measurement of time. Unfortunately, the measurement of time and the perception of time stay linked only if periodicity remains constant. For instance, the brain normally operates with its data-gathering running at the same speed as cognitive and interpretive structures. A major problem with using a biological basis for time perception is that neurons aren't as tough as silicon. Things happen. The body's response to any overstimulating event is the immediate release of powerful hormones, one effect of which is to dramatically speed up neural firing rates in certain higher brain areas. It makes excellent sense to increase the speed of data input when something really exciting or dangerous may be happening. Neural firing can speed up by 300%.

The problem this causes with perception is that by gulping down information faster, it can make the world seem to slow down at the same time. This effect, described in greater detail in Chapter 9, is analogous to the speeding up of a movie camera in order to create the illusion of slow motion. When parts of the brain get out of synchrony, all sorts of weird things start happening. Since this suggests that the perception of time must be a variable, it could give even Albert Einstein a headache. If time and space are interdependent, but time is a variable relative to the observer, is space also then a variable? Can we experience infinite space like a moment of timelessness? If we oxygen-deprive the brain, are we in another time and space or are we in brain failure? How can we ever really know anything for certain unless our knower is standardized, when we know full well that all human brains differ slightly from each other?

Even worse, biochemically speaking, at the molecular level, every thought changes our brain chemistry a little. Heisenberg's classic uncertainty principle states that since we can't observe anything without pushing it a little with whatever we find it with, even a photon, we never really locate anything exactly because we just moved it by finding it. If we can't think about anything without modifying neurons each time we think, what does that have to say, ultimately, about the nature of any search for ultimate answers? Wouldn't the questions change as the questioner changed in the process of working out any answers? Or is our mental journey the answer to life itself?

Questions like this are bound to arise as we begin to explore some of the operational aspects of our biological lens of perception. The answers do not deny religion, but just as the incomparable is unthinkable, the sense of time itself is probably a fairly recently evolved capability. If we could neither recall nor project very well, we might not ever think about what happens after death until it was far too late. In fact it seems highly likely that most, if not all, of those hard questions requiring religious answers may not have been possible to conceptualize more than a half million years ago. Recent discoveries indicate that the ability to sequence time, generate abstract thought, and speak all require brain structures evolved within a very recent time frame. The earliest humans with larynxes like us, for instance, didn't appear until nearly 200,000 B.C.

For Adam to hear God's commands, or even speak with Eve, he required a well developed speech cortex. Clearly, any Eden had to appear at least past that point in our evolution. In fact, without many recently evolved neurological capabilities, we would not have had the consciousness to know either natural law or divine intent, and even if we did, we certainly could not have written it, read it, nor spoken about it to anyone else. As far as our world religions are concerned, not one is more than 5,000 years old; organized religions are actually rather recent phenomena. Just as we ourselves are. If there were prophets before we developed speech, certainly no one ever mentioned it.

Everything in 1,400 cc's

All forms of consciousness seem to require two parts: perception, the ability to extract useful information from the environment, and cognition, the manner in which that information triggers a useful reaction. Limiting either limits our experience. Without perception we would have nothing to think about; unless it were for some purpose, we would have no reason to think. When the manipulation of perception and memory to some useful end includes the use of abstract thought, we call it reasoning. It is levels of reasoning and perception which we call "intelligence."

When it comes to judging the consciousness of another creature it is useful to remember these variables. The honeybee, for instance, perceives and is conscious of ultra-violet light. It can see colors that we cannot imagine or know in any way. On the other hand, a bee's tiny "brain" is so small that it lacks room for cognitive processing. It cannot adapt or decide anything consciously. It cannot reason at all. Moreover, its minimal insect consciousness must act through a nervous system of great simplicity and efficiency, and the bee is further limited by this simplicity. Insects are practically hard-wired, entirely pre-programmed. If a bee heading in a beeline meets a breeze, increased air pressure on one side of its body automatically energizes a muscle linkage that angles the beating wings, like helicopter rotors, to compensate for the sideways drift. The bee doesn't know it happened.

Returning with nectar or pollen, it dances directions to the flowers, turning in patterns on the hive wall as the other bees brush up to get the latest travel reports. It would be nice to imagine that bees are scrupulously honest insects, since not once has a bad bee knowingly passed on false information. In fact they can't. It's the playback of a flight recorder operating the bee, turning the insect into a dancing marionette mindlessly miming something it can never understand. Aside from lacking alternatives, insect brains have little internal redundancy because insects wear out before they need replacement parts. Four generations of honey bees live and die during the time it takes one human brain to mature; four years during which our unique human consciousness acquires complexities and capabilities we can never fully comprehend.

To know the soul, it must be perceived by a human consciousness for examination and reflection. For love to guide us, we must be conscious and aware of love. If we are unaware of ourselves or others, we are called thoughtless. When we act without the awareness available to us, we are not being mindful. It is our consciousness alone that makes the universe known to us; and our consciousness is made known to us, moment to moment, only through the functioning of our living brain.

Within the space of roughly fourteen hundred cubic centimeters moves the exquisite organic instrument which determines our entire awareness of anything else at all. Damage it or stress it and we are no longer aware of anything in the same manner. Our universe will change around us. We may have a change of heart, we can change our minds, and the brain will accommodate our shifting realities without a missing a beat. But if we tamper with any basic function of the brain, we can distort or destroy the perception, realization, and projection of our entire consciousness for some time, possibly for all time. Our world, as we know it, is in our hands. More precisely, it is in our heads. It is here where the paradox of mating the physical brain with the non-physical mind, spirit, or soul may at least be partially resolved. Whether our consciousness, with which we perceive everything else, is created by the brain, or simply perceived by the brain, it still can only be as we perceive it. We perceive all of it through the structure and the function of the human brain, the most complex and intricately arranged form of matter we could know or imagine.

The brain must function at a level beyond description as it must be complex enough to let us to perceive anything we can describe as well as run everything else at the same time. It is as close to the infinite as we can get close to, and it is not out there. It is in us, a part of us that makes us who we are and what we are and it is alive and well. It makes for us the only world we know, a physical activity that lets us perceive our days, our nights, our dreams, our faith, our beliefs, and any other thing we can perceive at all. Whenever we use our mind to search for meaning, we will find it wherever we look the hardest and we will always find it to be made of whatever we believe in the most. If we sense that the universe is in a constant state of creation and change, it may be because we perceive it with a living mind, born of a living brain, itself in a constant state of creation and change, a daily ongoing enterprise of many billions, perhaps trillions, of minute living cells.

Cells to Think With: The Binary Brain

Human neurons are complex, efficient, and interconnected at a level of sophistication not found in most other living creatures. Even observing one neuron going about its solitary business is to witness extraordinarily complex activity. Aside from the life support functions of metabolizing glucose and oxygen and housekeeping all sorts of chemicals and hormones, each cell is always communicating with hundreds, even thousands of others. Each neuron has a unique voltage threshold. Constantly receiving pulses from thousands of other neurons, several times a second it sends its own pulse to its network of interconnected neighbors, a constant chattering of excitatory or inhibitory pulses. Any time a neuron's internal voltage rises high enough, excitatory pulses minus inhibitory pulses, the neuron itself will "fire," sending its own electrical signal downstream to join the chorus of thousands. If it gets a lot of sudden activity, it shortens the time period and sends the signals along in faster bursts to accommodate any temporary energy overloads.

It is interesting to note the resemblance between a neuron and a tiny computer. It has its internal instructions to fire when it passes a certain voltage level, and only then. Its life is endless cycles of averaging, pulsing or not pulsing, and resting; adding, subtracting, and calculating like a patient little accountant living on air and Twinkies. Several times a second it says "something" or "nothing," and then rests for a new cycle. This unfortunately leaves us with the inescapable conclusion that at some level every thought, feeling, and perception has been either stored or realized as an immense, unfathomably complex pattern of voltage potentials. Not only is this hardly poetic, it conjures up images of analog to digital interfaces chopping up the harmonious flow of life into binary bits like some primordial data-Vegematic. Once again we are confronting the popular image of the brain as the ultimate personal computer. Still, it makes perfect sense that the brain would have by now evolved to the most efficient way of doing its work. There are plenty of good reasons for using a binary system.

The underlying basis for binary codes in computers is that as long as one has sufficient speed, it is immaterial whether the computer sees the number 357 as "357" or as a long string of ones and zeroes. If the mechanism, or the organism, only has to distinguish between two possible states, it's that much easier to identify the signal against the background

electrical "noise" always present in a calculating environment, be it silicon or cellular. Everything can be simpler and more efficient. Since
computers are so exceptionally quick, they don't mind working in digital
and they have been doing so from the very beginning.

We had a small computer back in the dawn of such things, when the
first personal computers were still ten years in the future. It was dumber
than most hand calculators; all it really did was convert typed code into
punched tape read by a phototypesetter. It had a program with only
about 800 steps. It was functionally dumber than a sea slug, but impressive for its time. The poor idiot had to go through its entire program every time it wanted to do anything. Everything it knew was in 800 consecutive steps, a one way smorgasbord-on-a-track that allowed no devia-
tion.

Everything it knew was in those 800 steps, but it didn't have the sense
to go looking for anything in particular. We would hit the "A" and in
one cycle it noted that an "a" had been struck. It registered "a" in a little
cache memory and raced through all 800 steps again to find out what this
"a" was going to turn into. Then it picked up the tape punch code and
jogged through the whole shebang a third time to tell the punch what to
do. IBM made the keyboard, Photon made the computer, and Litton
Industries made the tape puncher. If anything went wrong, which was
not uncommon in those neolithic times, repair wallahs from a trillion
dollars worth of corporations would show up and blame each other as old
stupido ran around in 800 step circles.

Of course, those silicon solid state switches are very fast. So fast, in
fact, that our poky little computer would run through all 800 steps about
a thousand times a second. It was a manic whirring electronic conveyor
belt, hungry for digital bits. We'd hit the "a" on the keyboard and zap, it
was punched out on the tape much faster than we could think about it. A
device that gobbles pulses by the microsecond doesn't mind if 357 comes
in threes, or three hundred ones and zeroes. It has all the time in the
world; a relaxed sort of digital virtual reality.

Human brain speed is nowhere nearly as fast, rarely exceeding eighty
miles per hour, but it more than makes up for this speed limit with massive redundancy and complexity. Until recently, most computers used
the model developed by John Von Neumann in which computational
steps occurred sequentially. From relics like old stupido to multi-million
dollar Crays that zip along at megillaflops, programs progressed step to

step in an orderly, if frantic, pace. Recent advances in technology have made possible a new generation of computers built on another plan. These "massively parallel" designs employ multiple mini-computers to chop up computational tasks and feed them to a swarm of hungry little chips all at the same time, reassembling the answer at the end. The new thinking machines are multi-tracked and much faster. The human brain, composed of billions of neurons in a three dimensional matrix, is both massively parallel and three dimensional as well. "Unimaginably intri-cate" is both an accurate description and an understatement.

If we are to send information around in a complex structure, and the brain is infinitely more complex than any computer, it would be helpful to use the simplest codes possible. The binary system makes for far less confusion; pulses are simply "there" or "not there." Ultimately, if these multiple multiplexed interwoven codes are complex enough, we can ex-press nearly anything. As a result, all of our senses, both internal and external, send their information into the brain coded into a string of pulses. From the taste buds on the tongue to the tone receptor hairs in the inner ear, almost everything comes to mind originally as a pattern of ones and zeroes. It is the major business of the brain to integrate this informa-tion sequentially with any and all pertinent information available in memory and react to it, incidentally creating this grand virtual reality we call the experience of life. It might seem impossible at first that a con-sciousness such as ours could be adequately perceived through something as simple as a molecular Morse code, but it is not as difficult as it appears. As an illustration, let us take a look at how our brain "sees" a sunset.

Colors from Zero to One

First, we have to learn to digitalize visual information. Say for exam-ple we're going to make a picture of a tree, a ten-foot by ten-foot mosaic for a garden patio. We have only black stones and white stones and they're about the size of quarters, about an inch in diameter. With a ten-foot by ten-foot area, we could get a good representation of a tree shape with a patio-sized grid of 12 lines to a foot, a total of 14,400 stone-sized black or white stones making up the entire scene.

As it happens, an acquaintance hears of our artwork but his only con-nection to us is a one wire telegraph. One day he taps in code "have stones, have grid, send pattern." A pulse will mean a black stone and an equal period of time with no pulse will mean a white stone. As long as the system is understood, we can send 120 sets of 120 pulse/no pulse strings. Our friend can then reproduce our mosaic perfectly, stone by stone. If we want to make the picture more detailed and subtle, we would only have to increase the number of stones in the grid. At a point, greater detail would require a patio the size of a football field, so we could reduce the size of the stones instead. Retaining the ten by ten-foot format and using pebbles the size of tack heads, we are just expanding the grid to 1200 lines to a side. With that sort of delicacy, we should be able to produce more life-like pictures with a number of gray shades when viewed from any distance. Still, the entire composition could be sent on one wire with zeroes and ones.

By the same token, we notice that all newspaper photographs are made up the same way from lines of dots or no-dots. Most daily newspapers employ a 65-line-to-the-inch grid, enough to produce gray shades at a few inches. Any time we want, however, the picture can be unravelled into its strings of ones and zeros, sent through a fax machine, and be reproduced perfectly by a similar fax anywhere. Color printing isn't any more complex. Any visible color can be created with the three basic printing colors cyan (blue), magenta (red), and yellow, plus black.

A color photo is scanned with a laser beam. The image is broken up into lines of dots registered by photoreceptors and each dot is sampled for the basic colors. The information becomes four different recordings, one for each color plus black. These will control another laser that scans four negatives, line by line, creating four grids of tiny dots. The photo is now "laser separated" into its component colors, with one dot-grid negative for each color. We then prepare four printing plates from the four grids. This is why it is called "four-color process" even though many more colors will be represented in the end product. The paper is printed with the yellow, blue, red, and finally the black grids. If the original color was green, there are tiny dots on both the blue and the yellow printing plates at the same place, blurring to green as we look at it. Small dots from the black plate create a darker green where a shadow falls over a leaf in the original photo.

This is also the way we saw the delicately colored pink and orange bands on the planet Jupiter and the icy blue of Neptune. Instead of printing the colors, the photo-receptors on the spacecraft transmitted their binary strings directly to earth where they were used to control the colors on television screens. It was all ones and zeroes again, with slightly more complex breaker codes that switched scanning lenses to create the different color grids. In these days, the impracticality of shipping paper long distances has resulted in the printing of national magazines at printing plants located in different geographic areas. Using the binary codes of our modern scanning and printing technology, brilliant images are flashed from coast to coast in seconds and still look exactly the same wherever they are reproduced, printed, and sold.

When it comes to scanning photoreceptors, the human eye is without question unique in the animal kingdom. We share the gift of color sight with very few other creatures; every dog has his days, but they're all in murky greens, browns, and grays. Aside from the ability to see over 30,000 shades of color, we are also one of the few species with true stereoscopic three-dimensional vision. More important, we do much more with it than any other beast or bird. The wild turkey has a much more accurate eye than we, but they're real turkeys when it comes to the thinking part.

In the human brain, areas of the visual cortex which interpret the right eye are physically interwoven with the left eye's areas in natural patterns which resemble a fingerprint or a zebra's stripes. One of the most amazing things about the human eye is its ability to handle gradations in color and brightness from bright sunlight to shadow without altering color values; it never has to change film or rely on filters.

Between our optics and the interpretive ability of the various layers of the visual cortex, the human 3-D all-color-correcting sense of sight is the number one picture show on earth. Still, it is all in binary code. The cone cells in the retina register blue, blue-green, and red light. The rod cells, used mainly for low light vision, register only black and white. By a complex process known as color subtraction, not so complex as to prevent Polaroid from working it into instant color film, those three colors do the same job as the four basic printing colors, plus black and white. The retina contains several levels of cells which allow it to separate out not only color but edges and movement as well. With the delicate muscles and the lens of the human eye to direct and focus images on that retina, we have a natural grid with which we can register any visual image between the infra-red and ultra-violet ranges.

How subtle should we get? As it happens, each eye has about 120 million retinal cells. It's difficult to imagine using a grid of roughly twelve million lines to the inch, but that's what we have at our disposal; it's a pity to waste it on black and white type. Looking very closely at color printing most of us can make out the color dots at 120 lines to the inch. *National Geographic* likes to be special, and prints its color at 180 lines to the inch on their own presses. When we pass 600 lines to the inch the eye cannot tell printing from photography. At twelve million lines to the inch we can't tell perception from reality. We will never detect the retinal mosaic. The digitized patterns that appear in the mental theatre of the mind's eye are seamless and totally believable. We think we see directly with our eyes.

Each retinal cell is only capable of firing or not firing; each cell must come up with a zero or a one. Our massively parallel retinal grids pour their information down through three layers of interconnected neural networks to further define edges, shapes, shades, and shadows. This results in some data compression, but the long optic nerves which criss-cross their way through the lateral geniculate body and back to the twin screens of the visual cortex still carry eight million fibers, each fiber chattering away in strings of pulses up to a hundred times a second. This is all happening before we know that we saw it.

At twenty-four frames per second we watch films, and at thirty frames a second we watch television. Our visual images, also, are initially reproduced frame by frame at the very back of the brain. The neural activity then seems to wash forward, picking up meaning and context from other brain structures downstream. A stroke here and the victim might see perfectly well but could not make sense of it. Human sight is much more than a cellular camera. In 1992, a research team from Fuji Photo Film Co. created the first organic micro-retina: a sixty four pixel grid a tenth of an inch square made from synthetic rhodopsin that could sense movement. We have a long way to go.

A Colorful Line of Thought: Synthesis and Sunsets

So now we can use our inner vision to imagine we are seated on a bluff overlooking a rocky California beach a little north of Santa Cruz, looking out over the Pacific. It's a warm Sunday afternoon, gone to the last part of the day. It was hotter than we'd expected because we notice a little sunburn on the neck, now with the sun low on the horizon. The warmth lingers, but the breeze is picking up. With the day cooling off, it's time to just relax and sit on the grass and watch the sun go down.

There were showers in the afternoon, and a last gathering of dark clouds are scudding slowly off towards the west, blocking the sun while letting its dying rays pierce through here and there as it sinks towards the sea. Then, for a moment, the lower edge of the sun begins to drop slowly from the bottom of the lowest cloud, glowing at the edge of the sea, suddenly brightening the horizon and bathing the bluffs and the waving sea grasses in that unique horizontal yellow light that blazes out when the heavens are dark and the sun is coming from a crack at the edge of the world.

For a moment the sun rests there, suspended, glowing in deep oranges, and slowly sinks into the sea. The waves hiss up the sand as the twilight descends, the pink cotton candy clouds rolling to magenta and fading in gentle deep purples. Shadows begin to wrap the rocks in deepening darkness while the silver slice of a crescent moon, shining against the cobalt blue sky, begins its climb towards an evening star. The breeze is getting a little chilly now, and it's time to get up and head back towards the house, the windows alight from inside, glowing against the last twilight of a soft evening as a quiet night slowly cloaks the shore until another sunrise.

The brain remains in silence and in darkness. Sixteen million fibers are pouring cataracts of information over an infinite grid as our mind fills with the sunset, and we are surrounded by it in all ways. We can never be aware of those billions and trillions of ones and zeroes, we can never hope to see them although they outnumber the stars in the sky. It all happens so fast and so neatly that we see a real sunset, and only that sunset, in depth and color possible only for our human eyes to perceive, and a beauty only our human mind could know.

The sun has set; the grass crunches underfoot as we walk up the path to the cottage on the bluff. The screen door slams, Annie's dress waves on the clothesline behind the kitchen. Note on the table; "gone for pizza, back soon." The cat purrs by; it's time to wake for night stalkers. Cats have reflective retinas with nearly nightscope sensitivity after dark. Perhaps the cat savors another few minutes of sunset? A feline is quiet. Who knows what she thinks? She thinks in her binary code, her tail arched over her back.

But where does it all come from? And where does it all go? It seems likely that some basic images common to all religions might have a basis in human consciousness itself. As these images appear in the creation stories of many different cultures, it suggests that there might be some common explanation for it. It is true that we are recent as a species, and each of us is even more recent than that. We have not been here forever, you know. We have our beginnings and we have our endings. The only world we can care about is the one with meaning for us personally, and that world got its start at the same moment we got our start, at the beginning of our time, in the dawning of our being.

Part Two:
The Past

4

In the Beginning

From Heaven to Earth

The ovum is pierced. The genetic traditions of all our family ancestors spill into each other. Dancing chains of ribosomes, jewelled necklaces of life, embrace and entwine. Hesitant groupings of characteristics from both sides extend atomic greetings, bridging between with the clasp of phosphate bonds; twining, twirling, fusing. Now we are. We know nothing, and everything, because we are all that we could know. We are the one and only because we are the only one; a one-cell dream of a future self.

In that endless moment, the pulling and combining and joining is taking us from never before until forever after. Here it all begins. We are weaving into something that was never before, or will be again, but is here now, and new. Still in a time of timelessness, the fertile cell divides, and divides, and divides again. Patches of genes awake with specific organizing powers. The entire composition is re-recorded in every cell; and the plans as well. Here will be the feet, here will be the eyes, and here will be the brain. In the eternal darkness, our home is forming, and we are forming, and nothing is left to chance.

There is a place and time for every part of us, and we grow. And where is the mind? Will it reside in the toes? But those who lost toes to the frost became wiser for the experience. Was our mindful spirit nestled in our budding heart? Many hearts have been traded by transplant and there has been no sharing of the spirit. If awareness is to be perceived through the brain during our life on earth, it will have to exist in a very limited form for a while. The eyes are not finished yet, and there is nothing to see anyway. There is no place to store a memory; those abilities will come much later.

But we're here. We are here from the very moment that the joyous dance of life began, inalterably and completely ourselves and only ourselves from the moment of our creation, long before we had enough of a mind to think about life. We are woven into every strand, and from this point on we simply locate our cells, find a place to settle down, learn to specialize, and multiply. Now comes the long and endless sleep of quiet building when currents and connections less thoughtful than thought, and many times more profound, are forming that exquisite part of us that will allow us to perceive our life and introduce us to the world. We have nearly nine months to go. Nine months to create, bit by bit, the biological basis for a consciousness that will, one day, perceive our spirit, our mind, and our soul. Like all truly beautiful expressions of nature, it takes a time to come together, a time to bring us alive, and a time to come apart again. It becomes over time, takes us into time, and it will go, finally, some time after we depart.

In our embryonic brain, our first perception, our original mind, is oneness, and only oneness. There is no time to compare with this, because with only one there is no comparison. The time of oneness is always forever, and then the cell divides and we start the time of two. And then comes the time of three, and the time of four. As each new living neuron comes into being, our growing brain becomes by that degree more discriminating. By the time we are three months along, our brain was adding neurons at the rate of 250,000 per minute; by the time of our birth it contains between ten billion and ten trillion of the most complex cells in the body. It is more elegantly specialized and balanced than anything in the universe known to man, for it must perceive our universe, and balance our life within it. We remember none of it. We can never remember when we were all female, for instance. It is not until the third month that the male fetus produces the hormones that alter his body and brain to make him male. Males can be feminized, and females masculinized, by abnormalities in a mother's hormone ratios at this crucial time in brain development. Even severe stress during pregnancy has been linked to gender-related problems. A pregnant woman requires emotional as well as physical well-being as her child's mind forms moment by moment in the womb. It is impossible for us to remember when being and knowing were the same, even though it seemed to last forever since we couldn't tell past from present. In our own endlessness we were moving steadily towards a meeting with a world which, having never been experienced, we could never have imagined, the world that we call time and space, where we will spend some time and take our place.

There is a continuing controversy as to when we are truly human. Some believe it to be at the moment of conception, others wait until the fetus can survive outside the mother. All seem to agree that the child, once born, is very small, or a very young human being. But it is not a finished human being. The passage down the birth canal is not the final stage for any part of us. It is only a physical interruption in our maturing process that transfers us out of our mother when we can survive in the world outside. Survival being one of those things we hadn't thought about the week before it happened. None of us expect to be born, we all expect to remain in eternity forever. In fact at that point we don't really expect at all. It's always been.

This is our beginning, and this is also our ending; this is the eternal place we must leave in order some day to return. Nearly every cultural myth of the creation of mankind is just a broadly interpreted description of the experience of birth from the point of view of an infant being born. We had always been in no time, no space, all time, all space; our only name was "I am" and we were always. In fact we were about to take human form, and be transformed into a child in a mother's arms. It was a blessed event, but it was also a bewildering one.

The Creation Story

It is dark, with a dull redness during the day. The fetus's eyes open by the sixth month. We turn in a personal universe, growing more and more aware but still all-knowing and all-being. There have been sounds, there have been the murmurings of God, getting clearing and clearer. The fetus can distinguish voices by the eighth month. Through all, the eternal rhythm of our early universe, the heartbeat of the mother of us all, our own mother in fact, was washing our being with pulse of life, from the lives before our own life that was her before we were, beyond the beginnings of time. This is the rhythm we will always seek, be calmed by, and even sway to if we feel stressed, rolling back to the beat of our very beginning, that wordless prayer we all know.

For a time now, we have become alert to the changes; in our eternal darkness a new spirit moves over the waters. There are great movements, the voices become clearer. The Creator is about to start up the world for us. The powerful contractions begin.

The obstetrician said "Turn up the light," and there was light, and she saw that you were good. It doesn't take seven days either, but it is a pretty chaotic experience and it might have seemed that way as forever ended. And what a demotion in scale! We had been the entire universe, the be-all, he-all, she-all and end-all, and now we are being born again helpless as a newborn.

They turned on the lights; the crowd cheered, and it was a whole new ball game. We called foul. We cried. We yelled. We were really put out; literally, figuratively, metaphysically, and actually. Our mind wasn't started at birth but we must have been startled. Drugged with natural endorphins, we were shoved down that dark tunnel into the blinding light. It had been forever in stage one and now gasping and blinking and kicking our way into this new stage and now, suddenly, we were center stage. All newborns must dream a lot about the old days, wondering about it all. They spend nearly half their time in "REM" sleep, the dream state, even with their eyes open. They just can't believe it. Forever and ever; and now this utter confusion? What happened?

We keep waking to a new reality and we cry a lot about it. You can't remember, nor can anyone. We talked in baby talk, and we thought in baby thought; we can't recall anything about it very specifically because our baby brain was still so non-specific. Creatures that operate entirely on instinct, practically up to the reptiles, do arrive ready made. Just hatch them and they're up and running. Aside from their size, they are fully wise and capable, as wise as they are capable of being, from their first days on earth. Here they come, and off they go. More complex creatures take more time to mature, and we mature as our parts mature. We come onto this earth both unfinished and unorganized; we can't even eat solid food for a long time. There is no part of us that is, at birth, fully detailed or final. Every part was infantile; baby toes, baby nose, baby fingers and baby brain. Everything was already working, or we could not have been born alive, but there is a long time between appearance and maturity.

Every part of us had years to go. Our brain was far from being organized and structured as it is now; articulate, differentiated and working with years of experiential memory. It was a baby's brain, and it was about as capable of reflective thought as baby legs are for running. It still had to develop and grow further, and all the time it was perceiving and understanding as best it could with what little it had. Given our baby legs, we would stumble and fall, we were not ready for gravity then. Given our baby brain, consciousness would be equally incapable of the sure and distinctive method of thought which characterizes the adult mind. We were much closer to forever then than we are now.

There are several interesting aspects to the stages in which the brain matures. We are born with nearly all our neurons and these cells rarely reproduce. For reasons which will become clear, it would be impractical to have to deal with the constant appearance of blank, immature, or disconnected cells in the midst of things. Instead there is enormous redundancy. With trillions of cells, we can afford to lose a couple of thousand a day all our lives, which we do, and still don't run out during our life. Between birth and the age of about three and half, each of us a little differently, consciousness is constantly on the run as our brain hooks itself up and trims itself down to size for a lifetime career in data processing.

Each neuron communicates with others, sending electrical pulses down its main exit nerve fiber, the axon. The axon in turn splits off into numerous hair-like dendrites, tiny sub-fibers. An axon which has grown all its dendrites is said to be fully "arborated," from the Latin word *arbor*, tree. It looks exactly like a tree without leaves, dividing and sub-dividing from major branches to tiniest twigs. In this way, a single nerve cell in the brain may be in contact with up to 50,000 others. With nearly all these cells in place at birth, much of the next three years is spent in the gradual arborization of the axons and dendrites. Our chips were in place, but they weren't wired up. We have to make our connections before we can make self-conscious communication.

When we are about a year and a half old, consciousness undergoes a very significant change. Until then, the brain has been using a lot of energy to push impulses down those innumerable pathways. At this point, however, specialized Schwann cells start to wrap each axon in a fatty layer of insulation called myelin. This allows electrical impulses to race along as much as ten times faster while using far less energy. The brain is soon operating with much faster and more efficient electrochemistry, getting ready for the complex micro-movements which will let baby take her first steps. It is during this time of myelinization, as the process is called, that malnutrition can cause mental retardation in an infant. The infant brain is still very vulnerable. From the virtual reality perspective however, things must have really done a flip while we upgraded our basic operating system. We completely alter the pace and the perspective of perception, and we seem to do it imperceptibly. That is to say, no infant has ever noted the transition of reality from what we might call our "universal infant Jungian mythology" state to the "ancient real memory" state.

The proliferation of dendrites during the years of arborization is profuse, creating yet another effect on perception. No matter how a memory is recalled, it must be stored in some place that won't change significantly in order to be retrieved accurately. Complex memories would require either huge storage spaces or enough little storage areas to hold as much detail as necessary. Luckily, the complex arborization of human neurons makes this task possible. The brain never runs out of complexity. At maturity, with trillions of cells, each hooked up to thousands of others and capable of a nearly infinite number of electrochemical energy levels, there is more than enough for a memory large enough to let us learn new tricks at almost any age.

But there are tricks that the growing mind plays on us while we are still infants. Each neuron is becoming more and more complex for years after we are born. Year after year, the dendrites split and divide and grow, finally reaching their ordained locations and settling in for many long years of electrochemical exercises. Each month, our mind grows deeper. The brain actually reaches its greatest internal complexity in an infant at about the age of three and a half months. Then a certain percentage of our dendrites die off, leaving us with our basic neural networks, our unique lens of consciousness through which we will perceive our hopes, our thoughts, and our world for the rest of our lives. As our activities strengthen and reinforce further neural growth, this is the time when we reinforce the basic mental idiosyncracies which will mature over time into both our personality and our entire underlying image of our world.

By the age of three and a half years all major biochemical and structural upgrades are complete, although final maturation progresses slowly through adolescence. The rapid growth phase is now over, and the network is stabilized. Memories are no longer distorted or transformed by brain growth, they can be encoded, associated, retrieved and recollected. Even more important, with the pattern sequencing capabilities of the prefrontal cortex finally coming on line, "then" is becoming "then," distinct from "now." Children now consciously differentiate; they know they are little boys and little girls. Tibetans traditionally select lamas at about this age. The fresh mind is ready for training as we now begin to learn consistently from a recollection of day to day living. All of us, in all lands, in all families, gradually become self-conscious and socialization begins. We are not center stage any longer, but among others. We are coming into contact and context with the world around us, and every day more out of touch with that eternal world that was ours, and was us, ages and ages ago.

Only before we could perceive ourselves in context could we be ourselves in essence. We had been like that for such a long time, with birth itself just a major incident. For years afterward, the world turns in sympathy with the churning activity of our budding baby brain as we weave our way to self-conscious thought. We enter this world not all at once, but by degrees.

There is always a mystery in our earliest beginnings. In his poem *Intimations of Immortality From Recollections of Early Childhood*, the poet William Wordsworth wrote along similar lines over a century ago:

Our birth is but a sleep and a forgetting
The soul that rises with us, like a star
Hath had elsewhere it's setting,
And cometh from afar,
Not in entire forgetfulness,
And not in utter nakedness,
But trailing clouds of glory do we come,
From God, who is our home,
Heaven lies about us in our infancy!

Those first affections,
Those shadowy recollections,
Which, be they what they may,
Are yet the fountain-light of all our day,
Are yet a master-light of all our seeing.

As author John Updike wrote in a 1991 essay, "The poet puts forward a considerably developed metaphysical explanation for the incomparable vividness and mysterious power of our first impressions." There is a bit of the poet in each of us, and it has its beginnings in that fantastic, never-ending world that we found ourselves in during our first three years. It was a different world, but our guardians were there. The first word for God must have been Mama and the first man to play Zeus in our life was father. It was our only world; and it was only there for us. We spent many forevers playing Adam or Eve.

Leaving Eden: From the Garden to Our Own Back Yard

Although this information about maturation of the brain has been available for some time, there has been little discussion as to how a constantly changing mental environment would actually be experienced by a growing child. It would seem obvious that if the system we are thinking with is growing more complex every day, our thinking will be growing more complex along with it. We are all familiar with the concept of infant learning, but we cannot hope to recall the experience of thinking with a brain which was changing so dramatically from month to month for three years after our birth.

It is such a long way from the relatively simple mentality of the unmyelinized, unarborated infantile brain to a fully developed adult consciousness that can read books and understand the words and so on. If the human brain requires four years to become advanced beyond any other on this planet, from conception to maturity, it provokes speculation as to our earlier mental stages. There are three fundamental aspects of the workings of an infant brain that is growing more complex by the month which differ greatly from a brain which is mature.

First, as early neural structure is simpler, our earliest memories would therefore have to be of a simpler, more universal, nature. Each day we are adding connections, so each day things grow a little more sophisticated. As young children we must be experiencing an evolving, nearly improvisational consciousness as we upgrade our awareness day by day. It would be like starting up a computer with the most basic operating system possible and then adding chips daily while revising and improving the systems architecture at the same time. The operating language would have to evolve to match the growing complexity of the circuitry.

A good analogy is the language we speak each day. No matter where we live, we know that our native language has its roots in earlier tongues. Ultimately, this all regresses back to whatever the original human languages were, and we know that they did exist. An American who spoke some German and studied Latin in college might know the ancestors of half his English vocabulary, but he would be lost in original Indo-Aryan. Likewise, our early personal memories are hidden in simpler patterns that a later mind can neither identify nor relate to.

Second, since additional dendrites grow out of the same neurons for years, early memories will be generalized even further. No matter how memory is made this rule still applies. If memory is created by a pattern of electrochemical values, it would modify as the physical structure holding it changes. If it is a quantum chaos pattern utilizing neuronal networks, it would be altered by the increasing complexity of the growing network itself.

Third, it stands to reason that those more recently evolved modifications to neural structure would be the last to mature since they would have necessarily evolved from earlier versions as later improvements. The more recently evolved forebrain and prefrontal cortex are associated with certain cognitive tasks which simply aren't available to the young child until these later structures are ready. The last parts of the brain to mature are the prefrontal areas, which maintain some of their plasticity all the way to adult physical maturity. The way that the brain matures is reflected in levels of consciousness that we employ for common tasks.

In 1991, neurologist Larry Squires, working under Dr. Marcus Reichle at Washington University in St. Louis, used a positron emission tomography (P.E.T.) scanner to determine the order in which brain structures were being used during recall. Matching word fragments to a list of words they had been shown and told to remember, his subjects used not only short-term recollection but also needed to match word stems with likely candidates in memory. A primary brain structure called the hippocampus seemed to be involved in immediate recall, but when the mind started word matching, the visual cortex lit up as if the subject were literally scanning a list of words in the visual part of the brain.

Finally, when the mind started searching the associative memory there was a "hot spot" in the prefrontal cortex as if this structure were now monitoring, or even directing, a search through the entire file of verbal memory. The hippocampus is an ancient brain structure, the visual cortex more recent, and the prefrontal cortex has been doing its sophisticated memory sequencing for less than a half million years. From instant reaction to reflective recollection we seem to activate increasingly complex levels of conscious recall, each level represented by a more recently evolved addition to our basic brain structures.

This leads to some provocative suggestions. If human memory is largely unstructured until the young child's prefrontal cortex is mature, we could not develop a sense of time until fairly late in our mental growing-up process. Our more generalized, undeveloped perception would dull the distinct differences between one day and another while asynchronous recall would eliminate planning. Months could seem to last for years; years could be centuries.

Meanwhile, due to simple brain maturation, memories of earlier images and experiences would be modifying and generalizing day to day. It's hard to form consistent images of a world remembered so differently from month to month during those three years that must have lasted for millennia. There's all the time in the world before we have a sense of time. As we progressed through our infancy, we all lived in a very flexible association with chronology. Until we can force the past into focus, time remains relative. Not until advanced brain structures are nearly mature can our experience be precisely recalled or even kept as a reference.

When our growing mind was the flexible place, we were the center of the universe. We were kissed that day because we were so loveable, not because mother won ten dollars on the lottery. What did we know of lotteries? We were spanked because we were evil. What did we understand of family politics or pre-menstrual stress? We were responsible for it all since we were the center of the only universe we had known since birth. Before that had been eternity, long before this extraordinary place where things kept changing. We went from pure oneness directly to both bliss and misery, from heaven to our own imperfect Eden.

It had been forever once, in such endless peace, then suddenly meeting these great powerful gods and demons who were alternately blessing us to dry-diaper-heaven, or condemning us to centuries in too-hot-bath hell. Sometimes it seemed like forever again, alone in the utter desolation of a dark, lonely room; only to be hugged back to paradise in a mother's arms. All babies are like that, all over the world. Details are merely cultural; infantile reality works the same in every little unmyelinized infant mind. We were all little angels, sent down to earth; we were all in that fabled garden once. Once upon a time God really did speak to all of us, thundering from on high. Probably about six feet high, but who's to know standing there at one and a half with a brain only half way through hookup, innocent of good, evil, and what will happen if we try to feed the

VCR a piece of pizza. But finally the image won't change, and the sequencing is clear. Finally we can remember clearly, seeing ourselves in our minds in a past also sequenced for reference. We become reflective, and begin to see our place in the scheme of things.

As our brains matured into memory and clear reflective thought, we began to pick up and retain both personal, and cultural, detail. Over a nearly endless time it happened. Our gods descended from heaven to be our mothers and fathers as the great saints and demons took off their halos and horns to become older brothers and sisters, our aunts and uncles. Bears and monsters became dogs and dump trucks as we graduated from the collective unconscious into the present space through a place of fable and mythology given to us with our baby food. Over three years of worldly time we are weaned from the world of our oneness and rewoven into the collective fabric of our own family and culture.

With the arrival of physical mental maturity, we finally came into this world. The tree of our knowledge is now becoming fully arborated, and the mind is ripe. We began to notice the many differences between here and there. The differences between me and he and she, the difference between good and bad. As we bloom into conscious cognitive comparative thought we are separated from eternity for the rest of our life. We are no longer all and forever; we are fast becoming one more lost soul in the here and now. Still, even as we all come to grips with the grip of time, there is not one of us that does not, distantly, remember in some general and diffused manner those days when the gods spoke. We remember the love they gave us, the love that we carry at the very base of our knowledge of this world. It was the earliest language we knew, the earliest source code of our sensibilities.

Our very earliest memories start with our parents and their natural love. Babies are treasured; there is no culture in the world that condones cruelty to infants. If there was one thing we discovered in this awful world that almost made the loss of eternity bearable it was the love we found out there. It is the only ration that we can take with us when we leave the garden because it was so simple and it becomes the one compass we always use to find our way back again. We know we must find our way back there some day, back to our old eternal home. We can't forget it just because we are discovering mortality. But we do. We all forget our first eternity. We nearly forget the love as well. But somehow we believe that it will all come back some time. We really want to believe that.

Back when days were months and months were years, we have the answers to why Jewish patriarchs and Buddhist "devas" had such extraordinary lifespans. When we were very small, naturally "there were giants in those days," as in Bible stories and all other creation stories. The years before conscious understanding are so different, because we experience them so differently. All mythologies start with a golden age; or at least a time when the gods were making sure everything was working right. It is to this earthly plane we descend, simply by growing up. Heaven is just an infantile perception of early life, and we were there.

If we try to think back to those earliest memories, we can almost scent the breeze of timelessness that beckons over that dark threshold. This is the true time warp, the undertow of trying to remember thoughts from another time, other lives, so deep and so vaguely comprehended, like fossils trapped in the very strata of our mind. We can hardly remember how long it was from age three back to age two. From two back to one is much longer, time for any number of "previous lives" as we move into our collective and universal mythical world time. There is more time on the other side of birth than we can ever remember. There is no time so endless, or so deep.

The haunting memories of those earlier times are still there, scattered and generalized through our waking perceptions; still alive in our dreams, and our nightmares. This is the personal and universal mind that is ours alone and, depending on how far we go back, shared with all others on this planet. The further we regress, the more general our entire consciousness becomes, the more time slurs, the more oneness in all things. The further we come forward, the greater the differentiation into all the specifics of our self in our space.

Only if the mind itself simplifies can we ever re-experience that other universe that has always been there within us. If the final maturation of our human brain forces us to forget that timeless place in order to deal with this time and space, no matter. We will rediscover it again at the right time, whenever something makes our mind simple again. It happens every time that we let go our nets of perception and find our centers, at moments when time stands still. In terror and in ecstasy the overburdened brain slips time for the moment. Then we can know things that we cannot express or even think about.

It happens every time we undergo an experience so powerful that it blankets consciousness, forcing us physically into momentary timelessness. It can happen temporarily, but only momentarily, and it keeps us aware that there is some place beyond time. It happens with eternal finality during death, the one and only experience that can actually loose us from the grip of time and make us timeless, before we die.

5

Stranded in the Here and Now

The Evolution of Time

Have you ever noticed how,
The time is always now,
Whether you're a brown-eyed cow,
Or a Mau-Mau,
Or an owl?

— *Michael Bridge*

Our earliest mind knew forever and our final mind will know it again just before death. This exquisite trailing off into the infinite on both sides of mature consciousness may be a suitable explanation for both beginnings and endings, but what about now? If we can close the doors on our comings and goings for a moment, what do these insights say about the present moment? The present moment, if we think about it, has been going on for quite some time. In fact, there is no time so timeless as the present moment. It has been going on forever, but our attention is often focused forward or reverse. The past can't repeat, and the future won't be here until it comes, but we think about them.

This ability to deal with the present while scanning both the past and the future is what makes human consciousness such a unique way of thinking. We may be the only ones who can do it. It requires huge amounts of extra memory, a very specialized ability to sequence it, and ends up confronting us all with those "questions that science cannot answer." We know them by heart. "Where did I come from?", "Why am I here?", and "Where am I going?" In the broader philosophical sense they become "Where did it all begin?", "What is going on?" and "Where does it all end up?" Our answers form the foundations of our personal metaphysics, our own sense of purpose and reality as well as our religious beliefs. Once again, the phrase "God only knows" springs to mind, and it seems that God certainly does.

All holy books, including the Bible, the Torah, the Koran, the Vedas, and the Sutras go to great length providing mutually exclusive answers to these three simple questions. They serve as the most basic philosophical dividers separating Shiite Muslim from Orthodox Jew, Evangelical Christian from Zen Monk, and Pope John Paul from the late Baghwan Rajneesh. If there are going to be some universally acceptable explanations, they will have to harmonize some rather disparate characters. Each religion has their answers and philosophical or theological structures to support them. Each traces its authority to a divine, or at least infallible, being and they all disagree. A Christian serves God through Jesus Christ, while a Buddhist practices compassion for sentient beings to avoid suffering. The Hasidim are inspired by the mandates of Moses, M.B.A.'s by the mantras of Mammon. Belief rules our lives, but there seem to be varying sets of beliefs depending on who we believe in.

The articulation of a personal or human *raison d'etre,* some easily encapsulated wherefrom and whereto of life, is what most prophets and philosophers do for a living. If they ever agreed, we would already have a world religion and it hasn't happened yet. Answers inevitably mirror the complexity, art, and wisdom of local culture; each a specific response to some universal human need to come to terms with these annoying mental puzzles. Questions of "being" such as these, which appear to be human specific and not culture specific, suggest again that we may be looking at an artifact of the neural system. How else would these queries appear consistently only past a certain level of neurological sophistication in human beings everywhere? Perhaps our elegant answers are just the echoes, the necessary response to something even more basic that makes the same mischief in every human mind.

Supposing answers were available. Would they be universally accepted? If it were the nature of human consciousness to ask the questions, any answers would have to fit within the personal virtual reality of each seeker. Any very personal set of answers would become a theology of one, usually regarded as monomania or madness. As a result, in our global society, most metaphysical structures are not personally specific but culturally specific.

The pervasive integration of science into the belief systems of nearly all world cultures has, however, provided us now with a common language transcending culture. From a neurotheological perspective, there is one glaring characteristic about those three questions which stands out immediately if we think about it: They can only be asked by a creature which finds itself in a past-present-future sequential time frame. This doesn't include humans until after the age of two and apparently the rest of the universe as well. For everyone and everything else, things generally just are or they just aren't. The concept of anything going anywhere in time didn't really figure into our own personal worlds for the first couple of years at least.

Why didn't someone pick up on this sooner? There is a good reason for this. New computerized techniques for mapping and scanning the living brain have revolutionized the field of brain science even more than the telescope changed astronomy. "Virtually everything we have learned about memory over the centuries has come from the abnormal, from people with brain injuries," writes Larry Squires. "Now we are able to carry the study to normal people, and study normal behavior, and that is very exciting." Mortimer Mishkin, a prominent researcher in perception and memory at the U.S. National Institutes of Health, agrees. "The information you can get is unbeatable. It has opened a window into the brain we did not dream of ten or fifteen years ago." Evidence is gathering that indicates that our sense of chronological time originates in specific structures found in the prefrontal cortex.

It was long known that some individuals suffering strokes in the prefrontal cortex seemed to lose interest in making plans for the future. One researcher who was interested in this was D. H. Ingvar, a Swedish neurophysiologist who had made a reputation with his studies of the comparative metabolic rates of various brain areas using computer displays of brain structures activated during specific mental processes. In 1985, Ingvar wrote "Lesions or dysfunctions of the frontal or prefrontal cortex give rise to states characterized by 'loss of the future,' with consequent indifference, inactivity, lack of ambition, and inability to foresee the consequences of one's future behavior. It is concluded that the prefrontal cortex is responsible for the temporal organization of behavior and cognition due to its seemingly specific capacity to handle serial information, and to extract causal relations from such information." The brain's pattern sequencer had been located.

This area of the brain is very recently evolved in humans and would naturally mature after birth. Jean Piaget, one of the great figures in child psychology, was able to describe a stage in development when a child, watching a toy train enter a tunnel, instinctively glances forward to await its emergence from the other end. Before that point, as soon as the train is out of sight, it's out of mind. Here and gone. The toy train's re-appearance seconds later is unexpected and surprising. Another train? The mental train of thought had derailed back there when the actual train disappeared from view. This ability to predict was called "conservation" by Piaget, and it appears by degrees.

The typical childlike perspective of constant novelty in the world is simply unavoidable if we can't sequence our memory. The prefrontal cortex is the last to mature, so we must slide into our conscious chronology past the age of speech. By the age of four, however, we are finally experiencing time in a sequential, three-dimensional framework. Gradually we learn to take such a world for granted, sequencing our past day by day in our memory and therefore, incidentally, perceiving time as moving forward. This may be how we perceive it, but it doesn't mean that time in fact moves in any direction. Perception is not always truth.

The brilliant mathematician Norbert Weiner, whose concepts made the computer possible, made a similar observation in his seminal work *Cybernetics*. Weiner reasoned that if time were to suddenly shift into reverse, planets circling backwards in their orbits, a space traveller arriving on the scene would detect no difference at the planetary level. Time might well run in both directions. However, it would be impossible for forward-time people to perceive a backward-time universe.

For one thing, any stars going backwards in time would be drawing in light, not pouring it out. Weiner pointed out that it would be impossible to see such stars given the way human eyes are made. Communication would be likewise impossible, since the conclusions would appear first, only to disassemble into totally meaningless parts as time receded. He concluded that the only sure thing that we could tell about any universe that we observed was that it obeyed the same laws of thermodynamics that we do. If we couldn't detect it, how could we really know? Perhaps "black holes" are the receding suns of other times, illuminating planets travelling backwards towards the past.

The present moment is always our ongoing experience, but we use our special sense of sequential chronology to give it purpose. Classical Greek has two words for time, *chairos* and *chronos*. *Chairos* is "just in time" or "at the right time" or "the time of your life"; the sort of time that is experienced. *Chronos* is sequential, the time we perceive as passing, and the time which we use whenever we remember, or predict. Once we know time, we know it's going to be all over some day. There is little wonder that the Greek god Chronos is depicted as a fearsome ancient Father Time. In India, the Sanskrit *kala*, time, became the fearsome Kali, the black (kalo) goddess garlanded with skulls who gets everyone in the end. Call your little girl Durga, Laxshmi, Tara, all the great goddesses; but never call her Kali, the most powerful of all. Only Shiva, timeless Shiva, could love Kali.

With the rest of the world living nearly entirely in *chairos*, the evolution of the human brain has placed us as a species on a chronological escalator travelling from the past to the future. When we began to sequence images from past presents, we finally discovered future imperfects and found ourselves confronted with anomalies arising from this specific new level of conscious timekeeping. Since we can't arrange time until past the age of two, we can't sequence our memories all the way back to the beginning. It's our inability to keep the time line within our own lifetime that keeps us guessing; we sequence back and forth like a ping pong ball that keeps dropping off the end of the table on either side. Since we can't remember those first beginnings, we haven't the appropriate mental patterns, specific or general, to predict our final endings.

If the human perception of time turns out to be an evolutionary step, it could expand our understanding of the mechanisms of chronological perception. At some point we must have acquired what may be a unique talent, and with it the host of time-related mental problems which plague us all. The moment we are able to sense the passage of time we never seem to have enough of it. Where did time appear? When was the branching off that set us on the road to the mind of mankind?

Time And Again: Making Time For Ourselves

There are two fundamental concepts basic to our perception of time. The first has to do with the sequencing of image patterns; the second has to do with the amount of detail we can store. The ways and means of memory storage are absolutely essential to the workings of information processing. In fact, the definition of the computer itself was originally as a device able to instruct itself from an internally stored memory. The more spacious the memory, the more complex the instructions and the functions of the computer can be.

As to how these patterns are created, it's a demonstrable fact that we simply cannot do anything in a physical environment without leaving some sort of physical trace. Total and complete disappearing acts happen only in imaginary places. The simple act of typing throws millions of atoms around, sending molecules of me into orbit and Taiwanese plastic into space. Physical events are no less disruptive in a fluid environment. Every time a neuron sums and fires, something complex happens in a physical environment. There must be traces left behind, both in physical molecular chemical changes and in the electrical conductivity at each of the connections. In fact, both have been observed.

Since the average brain has at least several hundred billion neurons, if we used less than one percent of its total capacity in reacting to anything from soup to nuts, it still involves at least a hundred million neurons. If an average neuron has about 2,000 dendrites, 2,000 outputs, the proliferation of one pulse down just one aborated axon would leave definable traces in 2,000 other neurons in the circle of just that one cell. Adding the other 99,999,999 neurons leaves us with numbers like "stars in the galaxy" for the number of tiny biochemical changes created at the moment we wake up and smell the coffee.

Smelling a cup of coffee calls into action a full chorus of cellular choreographies, all interpreted through our personal past experience. Neurobiologist Walter J. Freeman of the University of California at Berkeley describes the process: "When an animal or a person sniffs an odorant, molecules of the scent are captured by a few of the immense number of receptor neurons in the nasal passages. Cells that become excited fire pulses through their axons to the olfactory bulb."

"The bulb analyzes each input pattern and then synthesizes its own messages, which it transmits via axons to the olfactory cortex. From there, new signals are sent to many parts of the brain, including the entorhinal cortex where the signals are combined with those from the other senses. The result is a meaning-laden perception, a gestalt, that is unique to each individual. For a dog, the scent of a fox may carry the memory of food and the expectation of a meal. For a rabbit, the same scent may arouse memories of a chase, and fear of attack."

If we could recreate exactly those instantaneous energy networks, that individual fleeting electrochemical tapestry, we would not just remember our experience. We would relive it exactly, a perfect replay of the entire virtual reality we once experienced. Recall, in comparison, recreates the image or thought with a very incomplete pattern. It is as if the original perception had created a network of electrochemical trails as the pulses proliferated outward through those millions of interconnected neurons. Like the after-image of a brilliant firework display, the ghost of the event remains in the innumerable synaptic and intercellular changes created when the electrical energy came coursing through during first perception.

If microscopic dots on a plastic laser disc can provide CD music quality these days, we might wonder why we can't simply play back the past. The reason may be that the neurological "afterimage" is not only imprecise, it probably serves simply as the physical foundation for another pattern, a quantum electrochemical tracery invisible excepting as a mathematical event. The brain is alive and thoroughly interconnected; the ongoing process is chaotic to the extreme. Still, as a pole hammered into a stream will have a definable effect on the flow of water passing around it, so any physical changes, no matter how small, will effect the neural flow patterns in definable ways. This is why every thought changes the brain a tiny amount. Nothing remains unaffected; everything is always changing.

Excepting for rare neurological or dream events, then, memory is rarely replayed. Eventually, patterns not regularly reinforced by repetition or remembrance lose their linkages and dissolve in the unconscious. Every instant leaves its own record, it seems, but depending on the intensity of the event and the attention we gave it, the currents of time soon wash the labels off our files and they are lost in the warehouse of forgetfulness where they eventually compost into the general subconscious image bank we use for our imagination and dreams.

We had each moment in focus as it happened, and it was all there once, but unless we replay entire sequences over and over again in our mind, memories fade into the past and are soon lost to conscious recall. Studies by James Kreuger of the University of Tennessee demonstrated that during sleep the brain releases special substances, cytokines, which induce special firing patterns among various neuron groups. Kreuger suspects that since even major connections are not always used every day, this is a way of exercising them at night during sleep, preserving the connections for future use. Still, eventually all but the most extended and repeated networks lose definition and fade from our memory.

This is actually a blessing. If memory remained conscious, we would be constantly distracted. We are actually living in the present, so it is better not to have to deal with too many after-images on the screen of our conscious perception. Asked about his supposed powers to recall previous lives, the 14th Dalai Lama replied that since we should be attentive to the present, his apparent inability to remember a previous life didn't bother him. "I know people who cannot remember what they did last year," he added with a chuckle, "So not remembering an entire lifetime ago is not such a concern to me."

The physical complexity of our neural networks could easily encode vast amounts of specific data without altering the ongoing functioning of any neuron itself. Like decals on a racing car, tiny changes won't affect the speed or performance. Each neuron, depending on its past, must carry traces which enable it to be part of numerous interlinked patterns depending on the moment, but no single cell has to do very much or know anything at all. In a sports stadium display of rippling squares, each participant has only a few pieces of colored cardboard, a tiny part of the whole design. The image is never visible to the very people who create them, just like neurons, each one a little living part of the big picture.

Day and night, each neuron does its ongoing accounting while the happenstantial remnants of experience weave ever more complex and interconnected patterns throughout the brain. Some details fade out, others are reinforced and even extended by repetition; some interconnect to long lost pattern fragments, incidentally creating new internal combinations energetic enough to surface as sudden thoughts, ideas, insights, and intuitions. There must be unconscious but intricate muscle memories in the cerebellum, our experiential memories in the cerebral cortex, emotional memories in the hippocampus, and verbal memories in the speech centers. Although the hippocampus has a central organizing role, memory remains predominantly a function of the amount, complexity, and organization of available brain mass.

Regard the caterpillar, for instance. It hatches, eats leaves, spins a cocoon and turns itself into a moth if it is lucky. Its nerve cells are less complex than those in humans, and may have only a few hundred interconnections for each. But still, it has 350,000 of them. It needs every one of them to operate the 200 muscles it uses to chew leaf with and that's just for starters.

The computational power of a caterpillar "brain" soars over any super-computer we have yet devised. Computer controlled assembly lines can assemble automobiles with only a dozen or so process computers; the very idea of 350,000 little process computers packed that small is awesome. When our supercomputers get that complex, they will probably be able to crawl about and lay eggs too, as any caterpillar can. At this very basic level of mass and complexity, there is enough sense to run the caterpillar but it's all used up just operating the insect. The surest test we have for conscious memory is learned alternatives, and insects learn practically nothing. The longest memory span observed for an insect so far is roughly fifteen minutes for the scarab, or dung beetle. It actually remembers to feed its young.

We can employ operant conditioning and get responses back from flatworms, but reacting to chemical states is not education. If they had the minds to appreciate it, insects could be ideal Zen monks: always in the now, and always in the flow, nothing ever expected because nothing ever happens more than once. A brain that cannot recall a past cannot predict a thing. No crisis, no surprises; just processes. So it goes, forever.

As life forms evolved into greater complexity, their brains grew to handle additional tasks of monitoring and control. As the brain grew in size, so memory also grew until it was able to store enough acquired information to help guide an animal's activity from one moment to the next. Fish and lizards are difficult to train, but by the time the brain reaches 20 cubic centimeters, there is real learning ability. This much brain mass is, apparently, sufficient to retain enough experience to initiate some vague form of purposeful repetition leading to an improved interaction with the environment.

Complex learning appears after the reptiles and by the time the brain has grown to 150 cc's, a good sized mammal, it has excellent perception and memory enough to learn, recall, anticipate, and dream. There isn't enough capacity in their 150 cc's, however, for intellectual discrimination, philosophical meaning, specific self-consciousness, or even good three-dimensional color memory. Memory must be reconstructed from complex stored patterns, and most creatures simply have neither the capacity to store much peripheral detail nor the ability to sequence images into a conscious chronology. Without a chronological consciousness, animals cannot make any but the simplest plans based on the past. Even chimpanzees, at 300 cc's the smartest of the smart, have never planted a crop. The immediate future is all they seem to have in focus. If they could recall even a few years in sequence they would have observed and remembered the progression of seed to fruit and tried it out long ago.

Self-consciousness is also limited by memory, as we must be aware of the details which allow each of us to differ from each other. We know ourselves only to the extent that we recall personal past experience that affected us in the ways that form individual personality. Conscious and unconscious memories underlie our likes, our dislikes, our hopes, and our fears. As any sense of self is dependent upon the detail and subtlety of recall, the better memory we have, the more self-conscious we can be. Animals, for all their variegated plumage and behavior, are remarkably similar to each other. If dogs had character traits as complex as humans they wouldn't be needing their noses to greet each other. Reptiles are so lacking in observable personality that their manner is truly reptilian.

It is possible, however, to shame a spaniel and one can actually embarrass gorillas and the other great apes. Big brains do more than swell heads; they allow the development of complex personal and social structures. In comparison, an insect has no hopes, no bias, no conscious predispositions at all. It never blames, never criticizes, and it never complains. There is no self, no self-consciousness, no memory and no meaning. It means more to an observer than it can to itself. Its parts are busy operating at full capacity just getting the job done with a mere cubic centimeter of brain matter. There is no recall. There is no time for recall. Without recall there is no time, no beginnings, and no endings. The silkworm mechanically pulps some mulberry leaf. A bird overhead sees the silkworm, and recalls a meal. A human notices the bird, and predicting what birds will do to silk worms, shoos the bird away. The silkworm mechanically pulps some more of the mulberry leaf, a living fiber manufacturing plant with no time for silly things. No time at all. It pulps some more mulberry leaf. No time like the present; no memory of the past, no hope for a future. The silkworm munches on.

Although overall increase in brain mass provides room for better memory and a more refined consciousness, it should be stressed that evolution has never equated sheer bulk with intrinsic value. If that were the case, we would all be under the rule of blue whales. Elephants have much larger brains than humans and they are still using their noses for hoses and working for peanuts. In terms of species, from an evolutionary standpoint, whales are closely related to seals. A very big seal isn't more complex than a small one; just more of. Likewise, there is a lot of whale to operate and everything is more-of including the mass of the brain. Much more-of, but not better-than. Whale learning has been observed, and it seems to be at seal level, the aquatic equivalent of a smart dog.

This is enough recall for a sperm whale to dive down to where it remembers the giant squids were. The squid, with less memory than a paper clip, never expected anything in its life, far less a large whale in the way. No matter how many pounds of neurons a giant squid was born with, if they're squid neurons it is going to be squid smart and no more. Squid nerves are like cables, so big they're nearly visible. Compared to that level of simple consciousness, even fish are savants. In this world, it seems, any species that can't remember will end up dinner for the rest. It was our last upgrade, the development of sequential recall and projection, which finally lifted us out of the present tense, our mental ascension in the evolutionary development of human consciousness.

Strangers In Paradise: The Evolution of Chronology

Ever since Darwin, it has been accepted that survival often requires novel adaptation to a new environment. The latest great evolutionary surge in brain development started taking place about sixty million years ago when some daredevil mammals got tired of being chased up trees and decided to stay there.

If we are going to spend a lot of time jumping from limb to limb with a small bobcat after our tail, literally, there are some things that will definitely need improvement if one is not to become cat food.

First, it is important to shift the eyes to the front, like a cat, for the three-dimensional depth perception necessary for judging where that limb really is. Good color vision helps get the live branch rather than the dead one; it's a long drop if we can't tell murky brown from murky green. Both aid in finding fruit and catching insects, increasing food as well as safety.

The brain's visual area was pressured to expand because so much instant visual data had to be analyzed for trajectories. Most animals rely on their noses, but we can't smell our way across thin air. A little off the jump, a little off on the grab, and it's one more pre-tenderized tiger dinner on the jungle floor. Dealing with gravity in high places is high risk for anything that weighs more than a bug and doesn't have wings to flap. It must have rained animals until the forebrain evolved enough to transform kamikaze marmosets into decent monkeys. Over time, the cerebellum doubled in size as well, accepting new specific and more discriminating control from the higher forebrain areas for a much finer tuned muscle response.

Luckily for lemurs and eventually for us, adding brain tissue is a simple genetic adjustment. At the fetal stage, the brain is so undifferentiated that fetal brain tissue has been clipped and transferred to a patient like living tofu. It grows right in. "More brain tissue" is easy evolution; it's so much simpler than adding wings or claws. How quickly the brain can grow to aid a specific species was investigated by anthropologist Karen Milton, of the University of California at Berkeley, in a study of two kinds of apes.

Apes have a diet centering on fruits and leaves. Fruits provide energy, but are low in vitamins. Leaves are high in vitamins, but require a long digestive tract to extract them. As a result, an ape with a shorter digestive tract must eat more fruit to make up for its inability to thoroughly process leaves. Since most trees bear fruit for only a part of the year, even in equatorial climates, it means that a fruit-eating monkey will need a more complex feeding strategy to visit as many fruit trees as possible in a given period of time. On the other hand, it doesn't take a lot of brains to find leaves in a jungle if that's our main diet.

Spider monkeys and howler monkeys are about the same size, but spider monkeys are fruit hunters while howlers are leaf munchers. Although both apes weigh about the same, the spider monkeys are carrying around brains nearly twice as large as the howlers. Not being cat food may have driven us into the trees, but once we went arboreal, locating food was the next environmental pressure for a larger brain. One of our most distinctive evolutionary steps was the rapid development of the forebrain's specialized ability to recall, and re-direct, very complex search sequences.

When a monkey starts to learn a task, most of the brain activity takes place in the parts directly linked to the event, the visual and motor control areas. When the activity is repeated, however, the forebrain becomes the most active area. Once recorded, the primate forebrain seems to re-direct unconscious, pre-sequenced routines that are far more complex than in any other species. Just like the human subjects who seemed to activate the memory search from the forebrain when retrieving verbal information, this scanning ability started with the necessity to instantly recall, modify, and repeat a sequence of muscle patterns. This is exactly what comes into play if we want to learn how to play a piano, dance a tango, or take a flying leap to a swaying branch in the treetops.

By the time the apes had their aerial acts perfected, they were using the most complex sequences on the planet. Since they hadn't grown any new organs, there were few changes in the operational parts of the brain stem that run the body. It was the finely tuned higher brain areas which evolved. Sequential pattern comparison in color and three dimensions requires a lot of complex storage. In response, our visual and discriminatory areas added large amounts of new mass and specialization. It is said that the brain of the porpoise is as complex as that of man, but its complexities are more associated with hearing than sight. Primate brains are mainly visual: monkey see, monkey do. Perhaps porpoises dream in stereo sound? They never say.

It had taken all of evolutionary history to reach the mass and complexity of the original primate brain forty million years ago. From that time to the present, there have been dozens of diversions from the original line. Some adapted into gorillas, chimpanzees, orangutans, monkeys, and baboons; from ground dwellers to neo-arboreal apes. Most of them get through life with a combination of wits, claws, fangs, and muscle. Some lines opted for miniaturization and speed, becoming the old-world monkeys and remaining in the trees. Our branch of the family, out on the African plains, gambled everything on brain power.

There was no way to predict that the higher brain centers of this particular hominid would undergo such rapid expansion; natural law suggests that enough is enough. Still, nobody has suggested recalling elephants or giraffes for big noses or long necks. The extremes are there to define the norm, and there was nothing normal about this unusual brain. It just kept growing. The mass of the brain spiralled upwards, doubling its size with billions and billions of new cells. By two million years ago, it had passed 450 cc's and it was still growing. By a million years ago, it had doubled again to 900 cc's, and it still kept on growing. By 100,000 years ago it had reached its current size, a staggering 1,400 cubic centimeters of mass and complexity that remains today well beyond human understanding, capable of the conscious perception of time and space both in the actual and in the abstract.

We have brains in our skulls that weigh more than entire monkeys, each made up of hundreds of billions of the most exquisitely formed neural cells on the face of the earth. If it took only an extra 150 cc's to give apes the ability to predict, recall, and correct, what must have happened to consciousness when mankind strapped on a full ten times more? We cannot imagine because we have been thinking with 1,400 cc brains since we started to imagine. We always think with what we have, and we won't have appreciably less until we die. We will never know the sort of simplicity that characterizes the mind of any other creature.

What finally made us fully conscious humans, less than 250,000 years ago, was when the human prefrontal cortex, already used to direct the orchestration of muscle movement, acquired the incidental ability to sequence huge memory patterns into clear recollection, abstraction, and prediction.

In the primate brain, basic predictive ability is located in the same general areas for both apes and man. Patricia M. Goldman-Rakic, of Yale Medical School, a prominent authority in this field, determined that when the prefrontal area is damaged, a monkey's ability to search for a remembered stimulus vanishes. It can no longer hold onto its memory. Such a monkey would be able to use learned patterns to jump to a tree with fruit in clear view, but it could not remember to return to that tree the next day. Like the young child's toy train, out of sight was literally out of mind.

Using similar tests on humans with damage to these brain areas, she obtained similar results. In some manner, the prefrontal cortex is able to scan memory into sequential form, and back-load it into our consciousness as the sense of prediction. Without this reverse-memory bias, our attention can't seem to get out of the present tense. In 1985, two neurologists, P.J. Eslinger and A.R. Damasio, described the dramatic changes in behavior of an otherwise highly intelligent man whose prefrontal area had to be removed due to a cancerous tumor. He continued to test well, but his daily activity was completely without internal direction.

"EVR (the patient's initials) was not spontaneously motivated for action. As he awoke, there was no evidence that an internal, automatic program was ready to propel him into the routine daily activities of self-care and feeding, let alone those of travelling to a job and discharging the assignments of a given day. If these goals were presented externally and repeatedly, they triggered the expected actions. But when external recall mechanisms provided by relatives and friends failed, or when the environment failed to challenge him with situations that demanded a response, he resumed his relative goal-less, unpressured existence."

Writing in a recent physiology text, Goldman-Rakic discussed this unique ability of the prefrontal cortex to supply information not available from our immediate perceptions. "The prefrontal cortex can play this role," she explained, "because of its elemental capacity to access and hold 'on line' information relevant to the task at hand. It seems possible that many integrated higher order functions including language, concept formation, and planning for the future may be built on this functional element." It follows that, given enough memory capacity, the prefrontal cortex can "access and process information derived from present events and/or long term stores, to guide a response over the period of seconds, minutes, and possibly hours required to fulfill the command."

It seems that this is exactly what happened. Roughly 200,000 years ago, some groups of early African hominids began to move out on to the savannas. Farther out into the grasslands, trees were scarcer. The heat was intense, but in standing up, we could reduce the heat burden. We shed our insulating fur and developed sweat cooling. We became bipedal, a balancing act any bird can do but which we mastered rather late. We also developed varicose veins, lower back pain, and pot bellies as everything sagged downward. The rewards, however, were great. Bipedalism was more than a better view. Now two hands were free to carry weapons, tools, food, and babies. Just as important, the cooling system allowed for even more brain mass. Now every learned muscle routine could yank huge patterns through sequential steps. The erect posture tilted the neck up and allowed our skulls to bulge outward in all directions, becoming nearly a hemisphere with a face. The larynx descended, and human speech became possible.

Out of the tree gardens of the tropics, we began to walk the savannas of prehistoric Africa, and we remembered clearly, and we abstracted, and we predicted. Our brains developed a speech cortex to communicate fine differences, now discernible; concepts now clear in minds rich with images, ideas and speculation.

Wherever we walked, we defined our world. We named the beasts, the birds, and the fish. We named the rivers, the mountains, and the plains.

In the darkness of night, huddled together with the young ones, we named the demons that we all fear, and with a growing gratitude, greeted the morning sun with the names of God. The time had come for man, the planner, the only creature with a mind that could search for reasons; the only mind that had the time and the capability to find the answers. In fact, the sense of sequential, chronological time itself had arrived, just in time, and it gave us all the time in the world. In no time at all we became the world's best hunters and gatherers.

Many paleontologists now believe that the lack of any native large land mammals in the New World was the work of the first humans to make it across the land bridge from Asia. Like bands of ravenous caterpillars with memories, these groups of early hunters munched their way from Alaska to Chile just by waiting about for giant sloths to come home and ambushing them with rocks and spears. If we could have run like rabbits or flown like eagles we would have eaten them, but why rush when we have time? We just had to wait around and consume the big ones, the slower ones that never expected us to be there. They couldn't figure it out in time, and so it was never time to go until they went into complete extinction, most of them as some very memorable meals for our thoughtful, if thoughtless, ancestors. Early human hunters must have had a whale of a time.

The maturation of pattern sequencing in our prefrontal cortex finally gave us, as a species, both chronological past and chronological future. If we examine the area of the brain where this is all happening, we will note that it seems to be in that area so characteristically "human" in appearance, the bulging forehead of modern homo sapiens. If so, this may have been the last add-on, the last major structural adaptation that boosted us into the sort of consciousness we now enjoy.

Before we could consciously manipulate sequential images, memory could still provide a sense of emotional meaning and a form of generalized past. Still, we wouldn't be thinking in abstracts or planning the future. We would lack the ability to focus the mind with any degree of accuracy. The sloping foreheads of the great apes suggest that the lack of a prefrontal bulge might well explain why gorillas and chimps strategize only for short term goals. It might also explain the eventual disappearance of the Neanderthal man, the human variant that died out so long ago.

Crimes Against Humanity: The Cain and Abel Story

The Neanderthals were humans, but they were not like us. They had a more massive bone structure, stronger muscles, and a brain large enough for human intelligence of a sort. They did not, however, possesses the rounded cranium and pronounced foreheads of the Cro-Magnons, and therefore may have lacked our sophisticated ability to sequence time con-sciously into a chronological continuum.

For centuries, scientists now believe, the two different species lived in the same parts of Europe. In 1991, a Neanderthal skeleton found at St. Caesir, north of Bordeaux in France, was dated to within 36,000 years of the present era. This prompted Christopher P. Stringer, a paleontologist at the Natural History Museum in London to declare that the discovery "demonstrates that modern humans and Neanderthals must have coex-isted for several thousand years." Richard B. Klein, of the University of Chicago, agreed. "Even allowing for some error, humans and Neanderthals were too close together in time to allow one to evolve into the other."

If the Neanderthals were there first, it might explain the sad demise of our last genetic cousins, those massive mesomorphs of the Northern Hemisphere. Judging from the shape of their skulls, with their back-sloping foreheads, it seems likely that their prefrontal cortex was not as fully developed. The absence of any preserved brain tissue renders any suggestions regarding brain structure speculative, but there is just not as much space available for this particular neural structure. It is possible, therefore, that their awareness of chronological time never progressed much beyond that of a human two-year-old.

The base of the Neanderthal cranium, moreover, is much flatter than modern man's, and unflexed. Jeffrey Laitman, anthropologist and anatomist at the Mt. Sinai Medical School, believes this indicates the el-evated larynx of a non-human vocal tract. The Neanderthal probably could not speak excepting in the most guttural sense: grunts, chuckles, murmurs and cries. Excavated sites have suggested that Neanderthals were communal in nature, that they hunted many animals, and, judging from advanced arthritis found in the joints of one skeleton, cared for their old when they were crippled or unproductive. Some have suggested that the discovery of bear skulls with unusual markings indicates the basis of a primitive religion while others, noting the existence of flower petals and pollen in ancient burial sites, have speculated on the possibility of Neanderthal funeral rites. Without a conscious chronology, however, this would be unlikely. Possessing unusually fine memories, they would be the cleverest creatures in the woods but their intelligence would remain nearly entirely present oriented, neither strategic nor analytical. In a grotesque way, they may have acted somewhat like a band of prefrontal lobotomy victims, demonstrating few noticeable mental complexities or sophisticated motivations. Like dim-witted *Night of the Living Dead* zombies, they spent their time digging roots, grabbing rabbits, or seizing a salmon for sloppy sashimi.

Excavations of Neanderthal campsites have revealed other aspects of their lives which also suggest a largely day to day response to their world. For one thing, it seems that the males and the females may have lived apart from each other and eaten different diets. No small animal bones are found near the fire sites, indicating that the hunting males weren't bringing home any but the largest bones and pieces, parts that needed serious hammering or heating to tear apart. Archeologist Lewis Binford points out this is hardly civilized. "This looks like we've got a situation in which females are essentially taking care of themselves much of the time. Fully modern man obtains food and brings it back. Then it's prepared and eaten by reproductive units. I don't think Neanderthals did that."

Furthermore, they do seem to be terrible planners. Every spring, rivers in French Neanderthal-land teemed with salmon, and yet there are virtually no fish bones in the Neanderthal caves. As Binford notes, "They're not bringing the fish home, putting it in storage, and eating it out of storage. Modern man plans months ahead of time; they move to places weeks before the salmon run; this all leaves a distinctive archeological record." There is no indication that the Neanderthals were lazy; it just seems they couldn't plot anything past a couple of hours. Binford believes that this severely limited their range. "Neanderthals simply didn't make it in the grasslands. To exploit the mobile herds of grass feeders, you have to know their behavior and anticipate it. Neanderthals didn't do that. They only lived where food was continuously accessible."

In the near future and the near past there is time to play with a bear skull or make a simple scraper, but no true craftsmanship or planning. Whether this mentally childlike state was a blessing or a defect is a good question for deists. It seems highly unlikely that a mind deficient in time and abstraction could ever come up with any of Bertrand Russell's questions. If the only answer to "Where did I come from?" is "From the woods, yesterday" then there is no need for a past with a purpose or a future with a plan. With memory out of sequence, abstracts could neither be conceptualized nor articulated and wisdom would come very slowly with age in a time when old was anyone over thirty.

Our personal years from birth until three included a Garden of Eden for each of us as our brains grew slowly towards mature perception. It seems that our brother species was wandering about in that garden for much longer, in direct communication with nature and wearing very little. Any gradual insight gained through experience would have been internal and inexpressible; wordless inspiration unshared and soon forgotten. Abstract concepts, such as the knowledge of good and evil, were absent from those massive but unmethodical minds. The real Tree of Knowledge was arborating in some other Eden; if any Neanderthal had met a talking serpent he would have eaten it on the spot without a further thought. Language recognition and a speech cortex wouldn't come until the next brain upgrade, rendering religious speculation mentally moot in the Neanderthal nation.

From a neurotheological perspective, the date of the creation of man becomes, like everything else, more a state of perception than a state of occurrence. Descartes said "I think, therefore I am." The neurotheologist says "I can believe only in what I can perceive." The question is neither "Did God create mankind?" nor "Does mankind create gods?" The question can only be "When did mankind develop a consciousness that could conceive of God, and what step in brain development might have made this possible?"

The oldest human skulls with a modern configuration, from about one hundred and fifty thousand years ago, were unearthed in Zambia at a site called Broken Hill. How long did it take for the capabilities of the expanded prefrontal cortex to bring us into abstracts, speech, and analysis? Did it happen quickly, or over tens of thousands of years? Nobody kept records back then. Like our years from birth to four, the first hundred thousand years of human consciousness are the startup years and we can barely locate them. In this time, we became conscious of the sequential comparison of our past and present experience. We became able to predict, to think into the future. We grew away from monkey see, monkey do. With conscious sequencing and projection, it was human see, human recollect, human predict, human do. Africa was our training ground for the future.

These future projections are not only consciously made, they are consciously remembered. Ingvar commented on this unusual ability specifically: "Evidence is . . . that the frontal/prefrontal cortex handles the temporal organization of behavior and cognition, and that the same structures house the action programs or plans for future behavior or cognition. As these programs can be retained and recalled, they might be termed 'memories of the future.' It is suggested they form the basis for anticipation and expectation as well as for the short term planning of a goal directed behavioral repertoire. This repertoire for future use is based on experiences of past events and the awareness of a Now situation and is constantly rehearsed and optimized." As we exercised our new future-vision projections, we became more and more acquainted with the idea of planning and expectation. The new breed bred better, fed better, and moved steadily up-country. It took a long time to get to Europe, but there were a lot of sloths to eat on the way. It was a hundred thousand year trek.

Modern Cro-Magnon type skeletons dating back 50,000 years have been found in Israel, predating the last of the European Neanderthals by well over 30,000 years. Neanderthals may have survived in Europe longer than anywhere else and they were well entrenched when the first Cro-Magnons arrived. In the European forests, 40,000 years ago, the local Neanderthals could never have imagined that the human brain had been upgraded 100,000 years before by a band of proto-pygmies in Africa. The arrival of the Cro-Magnon was worse than visitors from space.

She was Eve, the first of us; she was short and she was African and she was the mother of all the mothers of us all. It was the dawn for homo sapiens, but good night for the Neanderthal. Her large brained children remembered their past experiences, and then sequenced forward mentally to their predicted future events. They had the patience to hunt for hours or even days based on their future memories, their planned expectations. They had predicted that the hairy creature would return where it had been yesterday and the day before, searching for grubs, berries, or small game. It wasn't exactly like outsmarting a squid or ambushing a wild cow, but still it must have been easy to have a Neanderthal for dinner. Like older children waiting for the train to reappear, they waited quietly.

She was nibbling grapes when the Cro-Magnons leapt from hiding, converging on the terrified Neanderthal with the weapons they had crafted weeks before in anticipation of this future event. Now, in the thrashing present tense, they quickly subdued their grunting prey. They probably raped her; later they might slash and kill. It was pure brute genetic conquest of the last other human species on earth. Still, over thousands of years, enough of those that survived, hunted through the forests, gave birth to a mixed breed to permanently influence the gene pool of the Western Hemisphere. Those strains of Eve's children that branched East began to run into *Homo Erectus* and overran them, becoming Asians from Dravidians to Australians, Malays to Mongols. Those that branched West picked up other traits that date back not to the image of God but to the trolls, the gnomes, and the yetis; our squat, hairy, muscular and bestial ancestors.

When we reached the last habitats of our hairy hunk cousins, it was the end of the road for them. The only being that could conceptualize God had been given dominion over the earth, and we seized our promised land. The Neanderthals didn't have a chance. They couldn't say a prayer and they didn't have a hope; they were caught in the gears of a clockwork they could never understand. When we arrived on the scene, we drove them right out of history. They were our brothers, strong and able, but unable to plant a garden or craft a killing tool. We outplanned them, outsmarted them, raped them, killed them, and probably ate some as well, perhaps with wild flower garnishes. It was our birthright, and their death warrant.

We became the only ones on earth, garrulous, upright and stiff-necked; cursed with the mark of Cain for the systematic murder of our last brothers on this planet. It is a curse we still bear, sacrificing our own in war and religious strife. Whenever we kill for the past or the future we revive and partake in that fearful ancient legacy of premeditated fratricide; the original sin that only a fully conscious human could appreciate or regret.

Part Three:
The Present

6

Only Now

Abstraction, Projection, and Time

*"That which is past does not exist, while that
which is future is nowhere discovered. And how
can the present shift from place to place."*

— *Nagarjuna*

If the neurotheological perspective puts its focus on the method rather
than the miraculous, it may not require divine authority but it requires
clear and reasonable explanations. The concept of memory sequencing is
not difficult, but if there is going to be a future sequence, why doesn't it
simply appear to be our past in direct reverse? There must be a way to
create new scenarios without adding anything from outside.

If we are to transform our memories into future non-existent states, we
must use abstracts to do it. Abstracts, qualities such as "red," unattached
to images, don't just grow on trees. We can't perceive them with our
senses, but we need them when we imagine any state that doesn't exist at
the moment. "If I were to paint my brown door red, I imagine it would
look like thus and so." This is a visual "transform," a view synthesized
in the mind of an image that doesn't really exist. It could also be called
the "cache future," a sort of temporary place where a red door might exist. We can do past transforms too, such as "If I had painted it red before
I installed the tie rack last week. . ."

We have plenty of images of the door there in visual memory, but we
do a mental transform when we start shifting the colors. We are intro-

ducing "red" as a visiting abstract, and with it we modify the brown door in our visual memory to provide an image of what it might look like if we painted it red. All images of the future are formed this way, by creating present mental transforms of real memories, new variations on real mental images from our experiential memory file. But where do abstracts come from? Pattern sequencing, in humans, may be our mental engine of abstraction, the ongoing source of the generalities which we use to create any future projections.

When we do a chronological scan through patterns, it stands to reason that we will have occasion to sort through many which may contain a common aspect. If we were scanning backwards through images which contained first a red bird, then a red flower, and finally a red butterfly, the "red" would register three times in a row, more perhaps than any other parts of the pattern. If this happens enough times, the "red" itself would begin to leave its own imprint, creating a pattern synthesized from other patterns.

The size and complexity of the patterns being sequenced would have a great deal to do with this. Our increase in cerebral capacity was spread over nearly two million years. The pattern sequencer made it possible for the finest, largest, and most detailed mental patterns on earth to be shuffled sequentially in a regular and ongoing manner. Virtual information began to appear in the mind which was never sensed in the world outside. Networks grew in response to these new patterns, and extended them in further synthetic patterns. We assembled the tools for conscious abstraction.

"Red" is an abstract, but once the "red" pattern is synthesized, we can predict what a "red door" will look like without seeing one simply by interlacing the image of the brown door in visual memory with our pattern for "red." The imaginary red door instantly appears, synthesized by a simple transform. Comparing birds and flowers to derive abstract colors is just one aspect of this capability. Much more complex images can also be compared, sometimes with interesting results. If one notices the way the earth seems to be drawn to the sun and interlaces it with the image of a falling apple being drawn to the earth, one might synthesize an impressive abstract such as the law of gravity. Isaac Newton himself once remarked, "genius is but the gift of analogy." The gift of conscious comparison, which came along with our most recent brain evolution, is the genius of humankind. It may have provided us the powers of abstract thought.

A good example of how a seemingly closed system can be original would be found in the area of fractals, mathematical formulas used to create visual images which mimic life forms in every way. Human creativity could build naturally on itself, just as fractal images mimic clouds and rocks with novel manipulations of a constant mathematical formula. Perhaps our experience of life provides the novelty that drives our personal brain function, the constant formula, into an interlocked, ongoing, original perception of the world around us, always different, but in fact always an interpretation of our mind. The Buddhist saying that the world we see is not a picture, but a mirror, speaks directly towards this paradox of our originality locked in the constant repetition of our own uniqueness in everything we perceive.

In this originality lies our ability to project and imagine novel situations. We can generate abstract information derived neither from genetics, nor actual experience, but through the comparison of patterns sequentially juxtaposed in personal memory. As we transform the image sequence forward, we find ourselves in what we call our imagination. We can reverse direction and do "if only I had. . ." We can reconsider, and in such reflection, we can regret, and learn from past mistakes. The word "pagination" means a sequential arrangement of pages; humans reflect and plan using imagination, sequentially arranging, transforming, and projecting images from memory.

This happens both consciously and unconsciously as patterns are internally sequenced by both reflection and movement, constantly synthesizing abstractions within the coursing dynamic patterns. This had been essential for grabbing swinging vines. If we jump to where it is now, we die. If we jump to where it will be when we get there, we live. The brain must unconsciously image a projected state, and then fire off millions of different muscle movements in sequence to get there. "Vine here now, vine moving this fast, vine will be there. *If* I jump now, *then* I am safe. Predictive synthetic thinking can be a life saver even at an unconscious level.

Automatic ongoing pattern sequencing can't occur in a computer environment because computer memories are reactive rather than active. Neurons are not chips, they are cells. The brain is not an immense digital computer lining up pictures like slides and peering through them. Each

cell is alive, and pulsing away night and day. Most of this random mut-
tering is too quiet for us to perceive consciously, but there is always a
mental background hum. This continual chatter, a backdrop of constant
activity, characterizes the mind at rest; the constant flickering of billions
of energy patterns as our cellular chorus carries on the ancient tradition
of mindless mental exercises, incidentally synthesizing our happenstantial history with the present moment into the conscious and unconscious
patterns we call thought.

We are dealing here with a living cellular structure and neural activity
that more than anything would seem to border on the chaotic. Walter J.
Freeman, who described brain activity as related to smell in the previous
chapter, believes human invention may be the natural result of a system
characterized more by chaotic, dynamic states than static patterns. "Our
evidence suggests that the controlled chaos of the brain is more than an
accidental by-product. Indeed it may be the chief property that makes
the brain different from an artificial intelligence machine. One profound
advantage that chaos may confer on the brain is that chaotic systems
continually produce novel activity patterns."

For the mind at rest is not resting at all. It is alive, forever mixing and
matching, mindlessly weaving memories into complex electrochemical
tapestries on a time horizon that never ends. The rhythm is as steady as a
heartbeat as every conscious moment is caught in our nets of memory,
rolled in abstractions, and cast forward again as our sense of the future.
Hindus speak of the universal dance of Shiva, the endless rhythm that
makes this world appear out of sheer energy. Shiva is timeless, and he
keeps the beat as the images and illusions of thought arrange themselves
into the greatest imagination of all, our uniquely human perception of
time and space.

This ability to derive conscious abstractions from unconscious activity
does not seem to diminish with age; in fact the more experiential memory
we have, the clearer those universalities may stand out. In a 1991 study
at the University of Oregon, Cynthia Adams asked a number of women
of different ages to listen to a story, and then repeat it to a child. Adams
and her fellow researchers expected that some older seniors might do as
well as younger women. They were surprised to find that the seniors did
better. They not only told the tales with less repetition and verbal bag-
gage, they expressed themselves more clearly and fluently. "When these
older women retold their tales, they challenged the stereotype of age re-

lated memory decline," said Adams. "It may be that as we grow older, we improve our ability to home in on the important themes found in information."

As long as age-related mental deterioration has not started, the ongoing experience of life allows us to acquire a larger and larger collection of images. Repeated scanning will highlight major generalities in ever clearer and more detailed form. It is this unique ability to derive general rule structures, hold them on-line, and use them later which, among humans alone allows the old to become the wise. It may have evolved originally to get us to the next tree but 1,400 cc brains provide so much more detail that we grind out abstractions without even having to think about it. In fact, until we accumulate a basic set of abstractions to use for transforms, we really can't "think" about things at all. It made human communication easier when we learned to think in generalities, and it made speech really necessary.

Like the details that separate us from each other, it is always the specifics in the major world religions which separate them and the generalities which bring them together. The leaders of the faithful always find themselves in agreement on nearly all moral and ethical issues, leaving interpreters and followers to squabble over details. As our cultures become more homogenous in the emerging world culture, we may expect this fascination with detail to gradually diminish over time. We may lose the details, but we may gain a common understanding.

Chimps and Ethics: Moral Codes from Neural Codes?

Projecting even a few minutes into a synthesized future is a great leap forward. We know that chimpanzees make the jump. Those familiar with chimpanzees know that even short range basic predictive thinking is excellent for achieving desired results; chimps can methodically turn apartments into disaster areas just searching for a little food. When surprised by their trainer in the midst of such shenanigans, they have frantically tried to point the blame elsewhere before sheepishly admitting their fault. They knew "if you mess up the place, then you will be reprimanded."

When the brain evolved the projection mechanism for "if-then," it acquired "should" and "shouldn't" at the same time. The basis of ethics and morality had their start when we learned to project and expect predictable rewards and punishments in our future for actions in the present. This is why personal family interaction during our first three years is so important. All of our most original lawgivers were, predictably, our earliest caregivers; another reason why holy law often sounds like a parent speaking to a child. When we can realize that we are indeed going to get spanked for deliberate misbehaving, we start behaving. Trying to instill this sort of thinking in a one year old, clearly, is not going to work. They won't know tomorrow until they get there.

Only when we learn the difference between right and wrong can we intend to do right or intend to do wrong. Sin, guilt, and karma all kick in when we start being responsible for our actions. We lose our innocence as soon as we know what to expect; even the Asian concept of karma won't work until we can form a real intention.

The silkworm mechanically pulps another mulberry leaf in timeless eternity. There is no memory in the asteroid belt, no memory flung about the galaxies. It is all happening now, and only now, and everything that doesn't remember knows that. If we really want the odds, the chances of there being a tomorrow are very good. The chance that either any specific past or future exists outside our own minds is infinitesimal. Naturally we have problems with time questions. They concern past and future; places peculiar to the human mind and personal to each of us. There is only our past, and our future and we made them both up ourselves, in our heads, when we weren't looking. They are a little different for each of us, and neither are real now. One happened before and the other hasn't happened yet. This is one of the hardest concepts to master in the neurotheological perspective, the likelihood that all past and future states are actually occurring in the present, and that the present moment may be all we can ever agree about in any detail at all.

Furthermore, if only humans do prefrontal pattern sequencing, the vast majority of the universe must have no sense of time at all. Only a brain of a certain size with certain structures evolved to a certain stage could ever sequence chaotic patterns. We have no way of knowing what any other minds might be, but without those capabilities, the most vital aspect of our human consciousness can't be there.

Unfortunately, since the pattern collections we use for our memory and projection, our past and future, are individual and personal, we come up against a further corollary. There can be no "where are we all going" because we can project only into our personal future. Who knows where anyone else is going? The information which each of us has collected, with which we judge the present, and with which we predict the future, is unique. The innumerable coincidences and sensations which create each waking moment before our eyes happen before our eyes only. As a result, we each have a unique and personal mind, a past that nobody knows, and a future that is ours alone. This leads rapidly to an unexpected conclusion basic to the neurotheological paradigm. There is no provable time but the present moment.

Real scientific facts can only occur when at least two people agree about something in the same time and space. This usually happens when scientists independently observe the same phenomena, or by agreement accept the validity of certain procedures and instruments and obtain similar results. As it happens, no two scientists, or any other human beings, have ever completely agreed about the past or the future. Neither have these two places been located by any form of apparatus yet devised. All our instruments make observations in the present. So do we.

From a strictly scientific point of view, then, nothing really happens except the present. Any other point of time would have to be a personal extrapolation or a personal regression by somebody, some person, a prediction in either direction using personal as well as generalized information. There can never be two people in complete agreement about places which exist, it seems, only in the mind. Generally yes, but specifically, no.

Our ongoing chronological time sense requires images from our version of the past, which no longer exists, for our projections into a future that has not yet happened. Nobody can vouch for us in either place; the only place we can get real, factual and agreed upon information is the present. A moment later it is already patterns in memory, modifying past patterns, generalizing and transforming into our future scenarios. If we shut down our pattern sequencing we lose both the past and the future in that instant. Without them, meaning vanishes. Memory is the mother of meaning, our lives become valuable to us by that measure. We can lose track of time in the mind; the mind that makes time for us and for the only universe that we will ever perceive.

Metaphysical Questions, Material Methods

It appears that we are nearing a reasonable perspective with which to examine some of those questions which required religious interpretation. In this instance, the answers to our "time" questions, "Where do we come from?", and "Where are we going?", become clear almost before a summary. No wonder these questions keep appearing. Our sequencer never shuts off while we're awake, and it's always weaving the future out of the past. We don't start collecting a chronological "past" until we're nearly three. The structure of our brain matured, and we can't change it back. As a computer scientist might say about our inability to focus either our earliest beginnings or our final endings, "It's not a software problem, it's a hardware problem." Once we go chronological, we simply can't mentally comprehend the simpler mental language of an earlier time with a timeless mind.

The present moment is the only real time that really exists in the synthetic sort of chronology we create; it forms the solid fulcrum from which we reach back to recall and throw forward to project. If we want to project forward far into the future, we have to reach that far back into the past. The deepest is in undecipherable patterns we haven't used since the age of two. It just doesn't compute. Our early existence is not on line because we upgraded the hardware and lost the modem. Time requires a setting, and we lost the lens we need to read our earliest past. Likewise, any attempted projection to our furthest future is always going to be totally out of focus at the individual level.

Since nearly everything else is, literally, imaginable, this unimaginable destination business is most perplexing to the mind. The "timeless questions" pop up nearly as soon as we can sense time, but it's a gone fact we'll never get agreement on "the final future," nor even a consensus about it for that matter. The best we will come up with, if we try, is our "best personal imaginary final future" which inevitably turns out to be a thematic version of our personal childhood with ourselves, of course, in charge. Our furthest future is projected from our deepest past, and both sides of time progress or regress equally back towards the present moment. Tomorrow is the reflection of yesterday; we predict the future with exactly the same accuracy as we remember the past. Both are as real as those images we remember, transform, and project. Both are nonexistent outside our own personal virtual reality.

Time is a human mental mirror trick that leaves us, like Alice, stuck forever in the middle of the looking-glass with views in both directions. We are only who we are; we are never who we were or who we will be; we are bound to the world that is with only our minds in the worlds before or beyond. We are now, and were now, and we always will be now. Yet we all remember another then, and project our eventual return to that timeless oneness, our own internal eternity.

This is where it began, of course, and this is also where it will end for us. Our sense of time and space, our complex tapestry of experience and reality; it all comes and it all eventually goes. It seems the problems we had with the "time" questions lie with the personal idiosyncracy of memory and projection. Something inside kept hinting that we did, indeed, all come from some same place, and return to it again. This is why all religions give us explanations for these basic questions, to comfort and to reassure us. Those explanations were bound to change over time, but the questions still confront us.

We may have answers now, as reasonable as they are direct. So where did we come from? We come from the undefined *chairos*, the timeless early mind, into the specific chronology we acquire as we mature. What are we doing here? We are perceiving it all and fitting it all into the patterns we have created through our own personal activities and experiences, each differently, all of our lives. Where are we going? Back to the same timeless undifferentiated mind that we came from. The cycle is repeated in each of us. We appear out of our own timelessness, we put it into our personal perspective and temporary definition, and then, finally, we must blend back into that same timelessness again.

From a chronological perspective, this takes a few dozen years to accomplish, but for each one of us it must take forever. If there were ever a miracle to be thankful for, it might be for the way we segue into the sense of time, and then transcend out of it when it is time to go. Time is our greatest trick; and the human experience of chronological consciousness is the best example of perfect timing that we will ever experience. It gives us all the virtual time of our lives.

7

Feel Is How We Real

The Meaning of it All

"The question of whether the world is nothing but a physical accident or whether there is a plan, this is the main question of every human being. Because the only answer to our suffering would be that there is a purpose in it, that there is a spirit behind it. If these would not exist, our life would be a hopeless business."

— *Isaac Bashevis Singer*

It is difficult to question reality. If we do it too often, they think we're neurotic. Still, if each brain is wired a little differently, it must perceive a little differently as well. The rarest thing in the world would be the most normal viewpoint of all, at the tip top center of the bell curve. We must be, all of us, off-center by varying degrees, experiencing our personalized virtual version of the shared reality of humankind.

Viewed in this manner, our own description of the world may not indicate any existent consensus reality at all per se, but it would always offer a penetrating insight into the mind of the perceiver. If our world is not a picture but a mirror, we might consider Singer, a Nobel laureate, as being more self descriptive than perceptive when he made his remark. Singer was a gifted writer whose tales of insight and wisdom, embodied in the lives of the memorable folk characters he created, are close to the very definition of the artistic mind. At his level of creativity, he would have had an internal virtual reality more vivid than any perceptual world existent around him. He died at 87 in 1991, fulfilled and famous for decades, with his brilliant mind apparently still overshadowed by powerful memories of suffering in a world long gone. The Yiddish word for such troubles is *tsuris* and there must have been enough of it once in his life that he still sensed it daily in his mental landscape, despite all the great good fortune and international recognition he eventually enjoyed. He still yearned for a plan, an explanation, a reason for existence, despairing if it were not found.

Singer was searching for the big answers. This is a common theme among the creative, but absent among the dull. Philosophers search for meaning as consistently as a walrus searches for fish; a sort of instinctual preoccupation. Of course Singer wanted a big plan. That's what all philosophers want. At the top of the bell curve, most of the normal people, less artistic and much less philosophical, are searching for big discounts and they want a deal. If they like it, they buy it. The Zen monk says, "Make me one with everything," so the hot dog man gives him a chili dog with cheese. Is life profound or is it just a joke? Has it a plan, or a plot? Are we saved or are we damned? Is it even worth worrying about one way or the other?

These eternal inquiries are more thematic variations on Bertrand Russell's question, "Is there a purpose to the universe?" Of the three questions "Where did it all come from?", "What does it all mean?", and "Where does it all go?", it is the middle one which seems to come to mind most often. Neural function may well be the origination of chronology and abstract thought, reducing them to the level of operational phenomena, but this doesn't answer the reality question. Is there any real meaning to any of it? Is there an ultimate truth? Once again the answers may lie in the way the system seems to work.

Considering the complexity of neural architecture, we must assume that we each perceive a reality both separate and equal, in greater or lesser consensus with our local social and cultural norms. We are like six billion human faces, sharing a common humanity but none really quite alike. It would be reasonable, however, that any rules that could define reality for us would be common to us all, even though they would underlie our most subtle and personal individual sense of being. If life truly is only as we perceive it, can there ever be any deeper meaning to it? To deal with this question, we have already travelled through many pages exploring the structures of neurological metaphysics from top to bottom.

The experience of life is the brain's virtual reality. Seeing sunsets with digital pulses is consciousness at chip level: the cellular mechanics of our human color vision system. Normal brain development and normal brain evolution brought us to adult consciousness, both as a species and personally, in a dynamic illustration of systems development over which we have little control. The acquisition of forebrain pattern sequencing capability for both time and abstraction is the human upgrade that models, and manipulates our current mental perceptions. All of this is built right in. It came with the kit and we can't change it a bit. We hadn't gotten into personal issues yet.

Discussing answers to questions about either personal meaning or ultimate meaning is, however, different territory. We now must venture into personal belief systems, a sort of mental applications software that can, in fact, be updated by personal experience. As usual, rather than answering the questions directly, we might do better to investigate the system that makes the questions and see if there is a little common sense lurking about in there. We may have idiosyncratic neural architecture, but the rules of architecture themselves don't change from model to model. Likewise, we all have a different fix on reality, but the system we use doesn't vary from one mind to another.

Tabula Rasa

Neurologically speaking, we are born into this world with brains as blank as cauliflower. Operationally we are living and doing a good job of it, but without a clue as to what is going on around us. From a meaning point of view, we are at zero ego, which makes meaning moot. If we are going to perceive meaning, someone has to be doing the perceiving and we have to develop that someone part first. A human infant takes at least ten months to discover that it is separate from its environment; it takes two more years to really get things straight. It is not reality that we needed back then, it was security. Without thinking about it, early experiences and characteristics help to create our personality, our unique way of dealing with our world. They happen without effort and they are entirely coincidental. Our very first perceptions start the ball rolling. No matter what sense is picking up the information, it is sent off to the brain for correlation and reaction. The brain, at this point, is quite plastic. The parts are still maturing, neurons arborating and pathways developing day and night as we head towards full human consciousness somewhere past the age of three. The basics are in place but the neurons are doing their compare and reset, compare and fire routines without a full arborative complement. Each time a pulse sends a neurotransmitter into the synaptic gap between two communicating cells, it changes the biochemistry of that gap. The pulse is actually relayed by the neurotransmitter molecules, which diffuse across the synaptic gap and fuse with the cell membrane of the neighboring neuron. Nothing is perfect, of course, and a lot of the molecules end up floating about like space debris. A percentage make it back where they came from, called re-uptake, but some never do. Every time that neuron fires and the routine is repeated, the synapse has more molecular bits floating about in its communications channel.

Altering a synaptic gap with more or less leftover junk doesn't have a great deal of effect on neuronal activity. Each neuron has thousands of them, one at the end of each dendrite. Still, there's more chance of getting a billiard ball in the pocket if you have dozens of them ricocheting around and the same may hold true in intercellular space. The net effect creates a drop in resistance at that synapse and more pulses get through. These lowered-resistance synapses are created at the moment perception or recollection happens. They are the physical byproducts of momentary energetic networks created by the billions throughout the brain every minute as our neurons send their computations out thousands of channels dozens of times each second. Every temporary energy network leaves its ghost in the system as well as reinforcing previous levels of molecular alteration already created by previous events.

A neural pulse will proliferate further along a lower resistance pathway, and so a second perception similar to an earlier one will utilize some of the pathways created by first perception. This will increase the size of the neural net as some pulses can now travel further than they did the first time, contacting and energizing a larger population of cells. This simple rule is the underlying basis of our sense of what is real. Our initial perceptions may be incidental, but repetitions can be more than co-incidental. We are soon being directed toward the repetitive.

Investigating synaptic change caused by repeated stimulation, neurologist Gary Lynch of the University of California discovered that repetitive activity by itself can create permanent physical alteration at the synapse level. In his research, Lynch observed that neurons in the hippocampus and cortex would remain more responsive to repeated stimulation for weeks or even months. The phenomenon, called long-term potentiation (LTP), has long been suspected to have a part in the formation of basic memory.

Recently, scientists have started to create "neural net" programs for computers which can actually "learn" in this manner. The software is so designed that multiple connections interact with each other, automatically reinforcing those pathways which get the most traffic. As early as 1985, computer scientist Alan Hopfield had perfected the first neural net software program. It was able to imitate nearly exactly the neural processing of a sea snail. The program not only reacted correctly, it "learned" patterns of attraction and avoidance as it encountered software equivalents of pleasant or unpleasant stimulation.

The sea snail, *Aplysia*, was chosen for the experiment because it has only about 200,000 very simple neurons, well known to all and identical for each snail. Of course, real sea snails do it all under water, and make more sea snails by the sea shore. Synthetic neural net programs, including some of the fanciest artificial intelligence software available, can never begin to approximate living networks in the multiple trillions, modified each moment in the living human brain.

We now know that any single neuron may release two or more different transmitters at a single synapse. Some neurons can switch molecules, like changing languages, and send different messages at different times depending on what else is happening in the body. At this time, the number of known neurotransmitters has risen to more than 70, and there is no end in sight. The relics of innumerable previous energy networks established by all these electrochemical changes are subtle networks indeed, but early repeated stimulation seems to reinforce early patterning with changes in actual physical neural architecture.

During the period of brain growth in infancy and childhood, then, increased neural activity seems to increase arborization at some locations. Some neurons will develop additional uptake receptors and even new synapses much later in life. The neurons in the prefrontal lobes, in fact, arborate late into life, allowing us to intensify or even alter aspects of our actual working mental system well into adulthood. In the infant, early experiential heavy traffic begins to build both major and minor pathways, predisposing the flow of any later activities. From our first perceptions this is happening, and it never stops happening. Our fetal memories were deep and timeless, but nearly featureless. Shortly after birth our neural patterning begins in earnest.

Since neurons fire, rest, and then fire again, an infant can continually enlarge a neural net by simply staring at something for a while. If the infant is in China in a basket next to a rice paddy she might be encoding a pattern based on buffalos; the infant in New York City might do pigeons. We all created patterns based on parents' faces and familiar sounds, on family smells and tastes and touch and everything available. Soaking up our surroundings like a sponge, we furnished our house of thought with whatever was there at the time. Our unique sense of reality is this unconscious network, the ancient neurologically entrained part of early memory itself.

Over time, simple repetition creates idiosyncratic collections of extensively interconnected patterns, whatever was most repeated during those times that our early neural nets were being created. If there were a friendly dog in the home, we made early networks which have to do with doggishness and early abstracts about animals. The infant becomes a young child who is familiar with dogs, knowing instinctively some of the general signals that distinguish playful from menacing.

These physical and electrochemical networks become far more extensive in the human brain simply because of its greater mass and complexity. Since our body hormones react in accordance with our perceptions, internally as well as externally, the size of the neural net begins to have an effect on our perception itself. The electrochemical energy expressed by the energizing of a growing associative neural network, less resistant and more interconnected over time, will gradually trigger larger and larger hormonal responses. Because of the extraordinary density and size of the human brain, there comes a time when hormonal reactions to the energizing of those neural networks can become equal, and occasionally even more intense, than our original reactions to the experience which had first encoded them.

Since several major hormones associated with levels of brain stimulation have very perceptible effects on internal body systems, we eventually begin to perceive a "feeling" that accompanies some perceptions and not others. It is the hormonal body reaction to the energizing of those neural networks, an electrochemical echo that is there in varying degrees depending on the relative size of that network. As size is a function mainly of repetition, our emotional spectrum is essentially a function of our familiarity with everything we know.

These feelings soon become our basic underlying biochemical check-point for the simple safety of past experience. It has happened often before, so it is familiar. We feel the way we feel when things are all right. It's making sense. Actually, it's making microvolts. As repetition begins to provide hormonal clues as to what is safe and what is not, the tendency to remain safe by repeating the familiar builds upon itself as soon as the infant is able to express choice. Getting small children to accept variety is sometimes quite a chore once their little minds begin to identify what they like and what they don't. As our personality is defined by the way we feel about everything we can think of, we become who we are largely because of very early experiences which largely create our basic mental preferences. Our sense of ourselves is actually an unimaginably complex pattern of continuing hormonal clues that had their beginnings in pure chance and parenting patterns, the earliest repetitions of our infancy and early childhood.

Our feelings, which accompany our various states of mind, reflect hormonal levels resulting from our brain's reactions to both our external and internal stimulation. The more neural activity we generate in response to perception, the more we will feel excited or aroused about whatever we are perceiving.

This is unique for each of us, and constantly changing. As Larry Swanson, a neurobiologist at the Salk Institute, describes it, "Instead of thinking of nerve circuits as fixed anatomical circuits that always do pretty much the same thing, there's a metabolic or biochemical plasticity, a real chemical dynamic in brain circuits that is probably different to some extent in different people." Even after the innate patterns of personality are set and neurologically reinforced, thresholds for triggering our pain, pleasure, depression, and anger are always being set and reset by the growth or the waning of our neural networks that react to every event, external or recalled. As experience and thought add further networking we feel more intensely about it, whatever it is. By the time we have encoded any routine deeply into our memory, we have thought about it and imaged it many times. Each time we did, the network enlarged, and each time we do it again it will enlarge a little more.

In fact, if we want more meaning from anything, all we have to do is concentrate on it for a few months and it will to that degree become more interesting and mentally attractive. For example, if we were to arise each morning for a month and sing the same eight bars of a song and then go out and stare at one certain tree for five minutes, both the song and the tree would acquire greater meaning for no inherent reason at all save the time we had spent. Repetition alone, even when adult, expands the net ever wider, creating both new associations and deeper reactions to repeated perceptions. Repeated prayers or mantras are a good example. Constant repetition can create both reality and feelings not associated with the daily interruptions of life but associated with quiet times of emotional and mental peace. Over time, both prayer and practice can in this way become sources of consistent internal stability and emotional well being, as comforting as a personal friend.

Progressing from infancy into early childhood, day by day our personal memory networks grow until there are enough solid associative cross-links to provide an ongoing emotional sense of general familiarity with nearly everything we perceive. Our world in fact becomes real around us, a mirror of our own memories, a memorial to the particular path we have followed. From this perspective, we might reflect again upon the sorts of pain and confusion which must have affected the early life of Isaac Bashevis Singer for him to find his world forever facing such futility. His tales often resound with humor, they are filled with compassion; but he himself was unsure, imploring the assurances of an elegant plan. As the neural twig is bent, so the arborated mind will grow; it is nearly impossible to erase such earlier realities. Children who get assurances when they need them usually grow up to be self assured adults.

Interestingly, the effects of interneuronal activity in the origin of emotional states can be illustrated with simple graph based on a parabola. In this linear presentation we can observe the effects of a larger and larger hormonal signal evoked by either sensory stimulation or interconnected memory networks. It is interesting to note the manner in which familiarity or unfamiliarity serves as the basis of nearly every emotion from ecstasy to terror. A line intersects the sense of "reality," dividing the external and internal sources of an emotional state.

The reason for this is because we react entirely differently to increasing stimulation depending on whether it is based on the novel or the familiar. If it is familiar, it energizes neural patterns networked and sequenced already; if it is not, the brain must speed up immediately to gather more information to determine a timely course of action. Whenever feelings start to arise, we can be certain that neural activity has increased. If the source is coming from outside, we're trying to find a fit for a growing unknown. If the activity is from triggering a large neural net, the hormonal "echo" tells us it is welcome or dangerous depending on our previous experience.

The mid-point of this graph is at the bottom, representing the mind at equilibrium, equanimity, where the mind's reaction to perception of life is not apparent to us as any emotion at all. This is true disinterest. Neither a positive nor a negative feeling is present. Our emotions increase by degrees, familiar on the right and unfamiliar on the left; null to pure joy on one side, null to pure terror on the other. The gradations are, in fact, levels of hormonal reaction to greater and greater amounts of brain activity. On the left side is increasing activity from perception without reinforcement from inner neural networks, on the right side is increasing stimulation from neural network reinforcement without increasing stimulation from the external perception.

Unfamiliar Information	Familiar Information	
Terror	Joy	+5
Fear	Delight	+4
Avoidance	Attraction	+3
Apprehension	Expectation	+2
Curiosity	Interest	+1

Equanimity

Perception usually overrules reflection, but at least on some occasions a great amount of mental arousal is clearly an internal, rather than an external, phenomena. For example, gazing upon the face of one's mother is going to churn up a lot of networks, usually positive, even if nothing else is happening. Likewise, trapped in a car careening towards a freight train is an example of rapidly increasing stimulation from the senses with little historic familiarity as to how to deal with it. The mind races to sequence and predict, but it is drawing blanks rather than reassurances. The frantic neural activity releases hormones that propel us instantly into feelings of terror.

Of course, if the person in the car is a stunt man who chose his dangerous career because of emotional damage inflicted by an abusive mother, the situations would reverse with feelings of excitement and panic taking each other's places. It all depends. Our personal emotional makeup is so very personal and so very idiosyncratic that even the ancient Romans had a saying, "*De gustibus non disputandum est.*" "There's just no accounting for taste." The mechanics of preference are, in fact, no more than a construction of familiarities, and likewise our responses to the world we perceive are entirely biased by this internal mirror of previous perceptions that we construct during our entire life.

For a further illustration of the way in which familiarity, or lack of it, form the basis of emotional reaction, there are the parallel parables of the book and the "bliffer." In the first instance, we imagine that we are walking down a sidewalk in a familiar neighborhood, thinking about nothing in particular. This would correspond to the point at the base of the familiarity parabola, the absence of either positive or negative feelings. Lying on the sidewalk ahead, we spy a book. This raises us a notch from null to +1; or interest. We know what books are, and here's one lying on the sidewalk. The "book" neural networks energize as we approach to get a better look.

As we approach and the image becomes clearer it is clear that this is a spiral bound notebook with what looks like the seal of the college that we went to. This is greater familiarity. The neural circuits energizing with memories relating to our college years increase the hormonal release to the level we associate with pleasant anticipation or expectation, +2 on the familiarity scale. As long as it feels good, we will approach.

Bending over the notebook, we see that it is indeed from our old college. The rush of conscious and subconscious memory boosts the hormonal level again, this time to +3, and we feel attraction. We are smiling and warming internally. The endocrine release initially relaxes capillary walls, creating a radiator effect, and causes the liver to release blood sugar, increasing muscle metabolism. It feels "good." More old familiarity patterns log on, increasing the emotional "meaning" of the situation.

As we reach down to pick it up we are amazed to realize it is one of our own notebooks, one that had been in a box that had been misplaced years ago. Our pleasure increases to +4, or delight. More adrenalin. More ACTH. Our capillaries tense with a shiver of expectation. We clutch at the book, bringing it even closer. Now we are really getting excited, because maybe this is the long lost notebook with the only address and phone number for a friend we had been trying to find for years. It *is* the long lost notebook! The number and the address are still there! We have now topped out at +5 , or pure joy. The entire day seems to have stopped in its tracks as the rush of hormones floods us with what we interpret as the joy at finding not only a familiar old notebook, but the chance of re-connecting with an old friend. If anyone were watching us from a distance, our rapid changes from one emotional state to another without any obvious change in the world around us would seem most peculiar.

In fact there was every reason for us to get excited about anything so interconnected with so many of our internal memories. It's the way we know the familiar from the unfamiliar, from the interesting to the delightful. It is our mechanism of meaning, the way we can use our massive memory to provide a much wider range of emotional clues than any other creature has available.

On the other hand, there is the bliffer. A bliffer is a quasi-android intelligent pseudo-life form from the Dwaroid galaxy, one of those going backwards in time relative to our own space-time perception. Bliffers are often given as pets to young zurks because they absorb bad dreams. They are trained during their autogenetic cloning to seek out any apprehension or fear. Like zurks, bliffers are metallic and communicate with vapor streams. In other words it's a harmless semi-living pacifier that fell out of some flying saucer passing between where we can't see and where we can't know. It is also unknown in this universe. There has never been a bliffer on earth before today.

Once again, we are walking down the same sidewalk. This time,we notice a little metallic object lying on the sidewalk ahead. It is unfamiliar, but small, and the increased stimulation we get from directing our attention to it is also limited. It wakens a couple of familiarity networks associated with small radios or tape players but there's no match. We feel curious; +1 on the unfamiliarity scale.

When it comes to our approach/avoidance, the first stage of avoidance is usually a form of approach. Depending on the circumstances and our feeling of security, we approach mainly to acquire more information so we can figure it out and fit it into some association. The bliffer is just lying there, so we pick it up to examine it. It "wakes on" and starts to warm up. At this point we notch up to +2, or apprehension. We start to tense internally. Then, as bliffers will do, it starts to hum. To us, it is acting really strangely as unexpected visual and tactile stimulation continue to rise without any internal correlation.

The mind is beginning to feel anxious with increased hormonal release. We rise to +3, or avoidance. We put it right back down on the sidewalk again. Now that it is warmed up, the bliffer tries to ask what is happening, but as far as we know, it just started to smoke. As the vapors begin to rise out of the device, we back off. This thing is really weird; maybe it's a bomb about to explode or something. We recall images of car bombs, triggering +4, real fear.

Sensing that a nearby life form is imagining a nightmare, the bliffer does what it was made to do and starts slowly sliding towards us. That's enough to nearly terrorize any unexpecting human, and we turn and run, with the poor bliffer, still trying to do its best to calm us down, skittering along behind us. We're scared silly, sheer terror at +5, the top of the scale.

In both examples, nothing much has really happened. In one case internal familiarities elevated us to a froth of excitement while in the second, the lack of those same familiarities had us running scared when no danger actually existed. The book itself had nothing inherently pleasurable about it, and the bliffer was harmless. It all happened in our minds. In fact, if we want to be completely mathematical about it, it could be said that joy is familiar information building up faster than we can integrate it while terror is unfamiliar information flooding in faster than we can get away from it. To us it is all kinds of real, but it's no more than perception, patterns, and hormones.

Does mental complexity have anything to do with it? There is no reason to expect that those on the overconnected side of neural structure would be coincidentally blessed with sluggish hormonal systems to compensate for their excitable minds. Like high rpm engines, they always run their endocrine systems at the higher end of the scales, living their emotionally vivid lives no matter what the weather. Racing motors run at very high speeds, and in experienced hands they are as safe as station wagons. The denser the interconnective network, however, the faster emotions would go up the curves. More pathways means more electro-chemical energy, which means more intense reaction. The over-imagi-native can fall in love after one meeting, all excited with hormones and hope. The paranoid can intuit real danger in the arrangement of towels on a towel rack. Ruth Richards, a researcher at Boston's McLean Hospital, has suggested that the emotionally vivid lives of those suffering from bipolar disorder may explain the number of writers and poets who were known manic depressives, including Shelly, Byron, Hemingway and Woolf. The dull rarely get emotional about anything that isn't obvi-ous and often don't sense danger until it is nearly too late. Each of us is completely different.

The way that familiarity eventually weaves meaning around us was de-scribed by neurophysiologist Jonathan B.B. Earle, of Bradford College in Massachusetts. Earle noted that both drug and meditation-induced hal-lucinations develop in a characteristic three part sequence. In the first stage, one is aware of what seems to be a meaningless pattern; a visual hallucination, a mantra, a mandala, meaningless images or a jumble of sounds. After a time, the patterns begin to take on personal meaning, and fear gives way to acceptance and a sense of understanding. Finally, the individual feels a sense of actually merging into the pattern, taking part in a meaningful experience no longer confusing, but actually reassuring.

This is but a rapid example of exactly what happens to each of us over time as memories and predispositions urge us to repeat and repeat enough to drive their associations deeply into the most basic structures of the brain. All during our lives this gradual progression is repeated. The graduate student during the first semester at law school is awash in terms and torts, contracts and court procedures, trying to make sense of it all. By the end of three years, the theory and the systems of law have become a complex and comfortable structure with both meaning and purpose. The early confusion of law school transforms in a chronological pro-gression into the comfort of a legal career. After ten years of legal prac-tice, the structures and systems of law have become an inseparable part of the lawyer's daily life and thought, now thoroughly integrated into both self image and life direction. Once intimidating, the practice of law is now reassuring.

In a like manner, we are all originally confronted with life as a confusing mass of stimulations and perceptions. Gradually, as we moved into our self-repeating repertoire of likes and dislikes we find ourselves drawn towards the patterns and images which are most agreeable to those internal patterns we have already woven through our repeated experiences. Finally, over time, as we become familiar and expert, our own lives begin to provide a more personal and profound sense of meaning. This becomes the basis of an adult sense of self and our place in the world.

This self-creation of meaning is a frustration to our many attempts at intercommunications, but a necessity for any sense of personal validity. We perceive with a consciousness both unique and consistently idiosyncratic about what is real and what is not. If we did not have that sense, we would have no sense of ourselves either; without a personal outlook on life we would be reduced to herd mentality or ant-like anonymity.

Eastern philosophies seem to understand this paradox somewhat better than those in the West. The Sanskrit word *maya* speaks directly to this paradox. *Maya* has three translations which ordinarily might seem in conflict. Maya means "beauty," and it also means "power." But it means "illusion" as well. *Maya* is the power of our beautiful illusion, our one-person personal virtual reality, to fool us into thinking that anything has inherent reality or meaning beyond our need for that hormonal checkpoint, our search for familiar cues that feel real to us.

It is *maya* which makes us imagine that we will be young forever, that power is exhibited by money or intimidation, or that we are here only to be gratified. It is always waiting to trick us into believing that something in the world is awfully important, when in fact everything can be reduced to idiosyncratic perception constantly biased by personal memory. We see it, but we just don't get it. *Maya* is forgetting that every thing we sense is, in a way, only temporarily there and subject to change at any time. *Maya* is thinking that we really know what is going on. It's a nice thought, but it can't be true. We can only know what our own neural networks filter through to us, hopelessly biased and idiosyncratically perceived.

Only if that idiosyncrasy were eliminated could we experience the real universe directly. As long as we have the bias of our ego, we can't be objective in any way, not with a brain that operates with neurons and synapses. If we cleaned up all the incidental debris and rewired the nets practically rather than incidentally, we'd wreck those personal patterns and we'd be back to ant-thought again. We could all perceive the same world only if we could agree, even for a moment, to retrofit us all with identical brains to see how things really appeared when we were all perceiving with the same mind. This is not going to happen.

Perhaps the Buddha phrased it best with one of his more whimsical sayings: "There is no Nirvana without Samsara, and there is no Samsara without Nirvana." "Nirvana" traditionally means a state of no bias, no time, no space, and no ego either. "Samsara" is experienced as a life of futile repetition, likened to a fly caught in a vase buzzing around and around without getting anywhere at all. Nirvana is unbiased, untimed, pure perception while the repetitive and circular nature of life for most people, repeating again and again due to the tug of personal emotional attraction and avoidance, is Samsara.

There is no reason at all to suspect that Siddhartha Gautama was familiar with neural nets, or virtual realities for that matter. As an ex-prince, he was the junior executive dropout of the 5th century B.C. His statement, however, speaks to the paradox of reality that we all face. If we approach Nirvana, or experience it, we would be perceiving true reality in its purest form. To do this, we would somehow have to circumvent or eliminate every idiosyncratic associative cross-link in our neural system.

This is all fine and good, but it essentially reduces us to the level of human cauliflower again. Enlightened cauliflower perhaps, but without those crosslinks, incidental networks, and hormonal clues, we would lose our sense of meaning, reality, and our sense of self at the same time. To know ultimate meaning, in other words, we can't be we. We would lose ourselves in the very process. This might be fine for a last moment of conscious existence, but it doesn't pay the rent. Perfect nothingness may be neat, but its also without worldly value. It's nice to know it's there, but it's no place to spend a lot of time.

Likewise, whenever we think we have things worked out so that we are finding enormous amounts of meaning or misery in life, we are just overfocussing on ourselves. We're just getting a lot of excess activity out of our personal mental networks, hopelessly out of touch with true meaning in the purest sense. We can't know what actually is taking place around us because it's so entirely biased by these very personal filters of preference and familiarity. It's a paradox, but it is true. We can't have one without the other. Without the ground of meaninglessness as our base-line reference, we can never have a real feeling for meaning.

This sounds like saying we will never really find it unless we lose it. It is not coincidental that all spiritual teachers say that we will never find ourselves unless we can lose ourselves and reclaim ourselves again. As infants, when we see ourselves in the mirror, we are part of the picture. Not until ten months old do we know that someone is there. This complete lack of self consciousness, temporarily or permanently, lies at the heart of religious fulfillment. Meaning was moot in infancy; we simply were. From that point on, we make ourselves, and our sense of meaning, at the same time. Our personalized, home-made feelings direct us, they make our lives meaningful, and they bring us all the emotional pain and mental suffering we know. They are the human side of us, that part that makes each of us different from all the others, each equally alone, each equally unique, and each equally precious. It is by our feelings alone we are made heavenly, by them we have known hell, by our emotions we have been abandoned, and resurrected, and it will keep happening as long as we believe in ourselves and the meaning we have found in our lives. It is called the human condition, and we're all part of it. It may be a matter of neural nets, cross-associations, and molecules but it makes meaning and reality for us, every day of our lives.

The painter Marc Chagall died at the age of 97. Like Isaac Bashevis Singer, he knew life's darker sides. Born in Vitebsk, a Russian Jewish ghetto that endured pogroms and persecutions, he survived the Russian revolution and two World Wars. It was Singer's history, the very same, and yet Chagall saw an entirely different world, one filled with childlike joy and faith in the human spirit. As he once told an interviewer, "There is no secret about it. You have to be simply honest and filled with love. When you have love, all the other qualities come by themselves." It was the only world he knew, and he made it, and celebrated it, and painted it in all the colors of the rainbow. There was no plan needed. There was just lots of love.

Where did I come from? What is it all about? Where is it all going? The questions of human existence have their answers; over six billion variations on a theme. What is the purpose of the universe? It is what-ever we believe it to be and for whatever reason feels the best to each of us. Why are we here? Is there plan or purpose? Of course there is a plan; it is whatever we love to do or be. After all, what have we been doing all our life already but demonstrating that? We have made things happen. We have made others happy. We have conjured love, and endured tragedy; we have been touched by joy and we have been gripped by terror. We really have. Every moment of every day, in this world we perceive and believe in, we are the ones who make it conscious; we are the ones to give it meaning. For better or for worse, until death do us part, we make it real.

8

Energy and Ecstacy

Rats, Rapture, and Religion

Pleasure seeking must be, if nothing else, the most normal behavior possible. Pain seeking is called masochism and is usually treated as a form of mental illness. Looking out for a good time is the daily concern of all other living creatures on earth and a daily pleasure for many clever humans.

There are limits to everything, however. Carved into the lintel over the entrance of the temple of the oracle in ancient Delphi were two massive axioms: "Know Thyself" and "Nothing In Excess"; the original source code of the fine old Aristotelian mental system we've been using in the West ever since. These ancient axioms have proven themselves over and over again in the face of challenge from both sybarites and ascetics. If we get to know ourselves to the extent that we know our limits and don't overdo them, our mental systems will not fault out. Consciousness will not crash as long as we stay in the middle of its natural path. Once we get those two basic rules up and operating, everything else is applications software.

The only glitch in this program is that it neglects to mention just how we are supposed to find our boundaries. Until we pass a limit, we can't really know that we've exceeded it, and who exactly is going to tell us who we are? Self-definition seems to be fraught with personal bias and so whom do we choose to name us? Something outside the limits of our own sphere would be the only source objective enough to rule on our own validity, something beyond those limits we're supposed to keep within.

Coming up with answers to questions like these is what kept the oracle in business and she was farther out than all of them. A large portion of her working hours, it seems, were spent sitting over a natural gas vent babbling in brain-addled intoxication. This giddy glossolalia was utter Greek to everyone but the local priests, of course, who downloaded her random data into something that sounded like advice and charged a fortune for interpretation and interfacing services. This sort of scam, in our times, would be considered very much in excess of "Nothing in Excess." The oracle would probably be busted for drugs and her organizers put away for a variety of morals charges and gaming violations.

And yet, when observing the more expressive devotional practices of the major world religions, we consistently find something very similar. Swaying evangelicals, swirling dervishes; even swooning swamis seem to share the same beat. The repeated "Hallelujah" or "Thank You Jesus" brings the same peace to some as "Hare Krishna" or "Amida Butsu" bring to others. African shamans speak the same secret tongues as Oklahoman Pentecostals. The spirit of the Delphic oracle is born again as, worldwide, more and more seek a deeper communion. For some it may serve as a release from the rational boundaries of everyday realities, for others it becomes a personal bonding ceremony between the one and the Divine. All agree that whatever the motivation or the method, the faithful do seem to enjoy the many forms of transcendental pleasure seeking.

No matter what our culture the same themes keep reappearing these days. "Born Again," "Awaiting the Rapture," "A Course in Miracles," "Bliss Consciousness," "Cosmic Consciousness," "Satori," "Samadhi," "The Indwelling of the Holy Spirit" and "The Uncoiling of the Kundalini." Looking out for a good time is one thing, but this worldwide revival in religious practice is really remarkable. What does a swing to the spiritual bring which is so sought after by so many? Have we transcended all the gradations and degradations of sex, drugs, and rock'n roll to a genuine search for the ultimate connection, or is this accelerating trend towards commitment and communion just a new height of selfishness for "me generations" satiated on worldly thrills?

Is this growing worldwide interest in the spiritual really evidence of an evolving human consciousness or just multiple cultural varieties of avoidance behavior, a growing desire to turn ourselves into self-satisfied believers and let God or guru take charge of a world too complex and threatening for the likes of humankind? Is this the bigger picture, or just abandonment of adult responsibilities in some romantic search for innocence in these stressful times?

Transcendental bliss, isolated by itself, is hardly a highly evolved state of consciousness. Many of us have heard about the unspeakable tortures suffered by lab rats, and a few have probably also heard about the unspeakable joys of some other lab rats several years ago. These wired rodents had electrodes implanted in the hypothalamus, a critical part of what is called the brain's "pleasure circuit." It was a pure connection to joy, and each had a button to receive as many peak experiences as desired. Oh rapture! The rats would sit on their buttons until they dropped from exhaustion. They liked it better than sex, they liked it better than drugs, they even liked it better than eating. Normally animals haven't the first vestige of organized religion but this was the cult of the button for sure. They were converted on the spot, blitz consciousness, slain in the circuit and fulfilled with all the ratty forms of joy. They sure saw the light, but the gods of their current redemption were much more interested in their hormones than the rodent hallelu-jolt chorus. Transcendental bliss, at such basic levels, is both predictable and easily reproducible.

Brightening our brain centers with that sort of impulsive ecstasy wouldn't be difficult. Human reaction is more variable, but with enough work who knows what refinement could bring? It is just hard luck for the priests of the button that normal humans have never elected for this sort of brain surgery, and less invasive procedures, such as electroshock, do little more than scatter the signals randomly. This can often derail a serious depression but nobody's described electro-convulsive therapy as a pleasant experience. This being the case, we utilize the second part of electro-chemistry, heading for chemo rather than electro. It can do the same thing and it's much more subtle. Whether it's a second glass of wine to put a glow on the evening, the touch of a special fingertip, the power chords of J.S. Bach, or the duck walks of Chuck Berry; we have many ways to travel. By adulthood most of us have learned a variety of culturally acceptable ways to alter our brain chemistry and our state of mind at the same time. What we seem to be looking for, or at least what we seem to be getting out of this, are various levels of desensitization and personality generalization to allow for a greater communion with the other who or whatever. From the glad harmonies of music to the blurring effects of social drugs, to the personal and persuasive rhythms of erotic sensuality, in each case we are taken somewhat beyond ourselves, momentarily becoming a part of something larger rather than the solitary soul we know so well. Outside our own self-definition, with momentary out-of-our mind perspective, we may gain essential insights to judge our limits and help find ourselves in our own very personal and virtual space and time.

Those insensitive to limits they discover may abuse themselves and others, but within bounds even intense pleasure seeking is acceptable. At maturity, our powers are generally measured by the amount of pleasures available to the excellent in any field of endeavor from mothering, to managing, to meditating. In most forms of pleasure, we note, the experience of ego loss stands out as a constant. The painter who loses himself in the creation of a masterpiece is the same as the career woman who loses herself in a project she loves. As the late geneticist and Nobel laureate Barbara McClintock once said about her research with chromosomes, "When I was really working with them, I wasn't outside, I was down there, I was part of the system . . . these were my friends . . . they become part of you. And you forget yourself. The main thing about it is you forget yourself."

If we could wire up monkeys to create pleasure, perhaps we could wire them up again to monitor what is happening in the brain when feelings we associate with pleasure are occurring. In fact, they put the wires on monks instead, both Hindu swamis and Tibetan lamas. In the 1970's, research psychologist Elmer Green of the Menninger Clinic in Topeka, Kansas, took his wife and colleague Alyce and travelled to India to observe and record the unusual physical and mental powers of trained yogis. One such adept, Swami Rama, was invited back to the Greens' laboratory in Topeka. There, under strict laboratory controls, he again demonstrated extraordinary abilities to influence and control both his body and his brain activity.

Ironically, the Menninger Clinic is located but a few miles from the very evangelical church where the first American Pentecostals "spoke in tongues" on January 1, 1900. The entire Christian ecstatic tradition began in Topeka, a form of ecstatic release which has since spread worldwide among many branches of the Christian faith. Swami Rama was close to home in many ways.

More recently, the Dalai Lama invited researchers to study with Tibetan Buddhist lamas. Observing brain and body states during intense meditation, the researchers were able to verify that some of the monks were able to voluntarily control aspects of basic body metabolism through purely mental exercises. Within a short time, versions of these practices were being made available in Boston, Massachusetts, as part of an innovative hospital-run stress management program associated with Harvard Medical School.

We are beginning to gather the hard data on the states of mental grace. There is a way to go, but we are getting closer to a point in time when effective techniques may be commonly available to anyone who wishes to practice them. It would certainly go a long way towards establishing the sort of global human warming we so desperately need. If enough people could find an inner joy it would be difficult to sustain any form of human-against-human suffering. Despite our proud posturing and bloody history, we are still primates: curious, clever, and skittish, but hardly bloodthirsty by nature. Given the chance, all of us just want to be happy and not suffer. If rats can do rapture with amps and Tibetans do it with chants, it probably isn't that complex.

Taking a careful look at all the varieties of bliss, the first question to ask is "What is happening in the brain when 'happy' is taking place?" What, simply stated, is actually going on up there when someone is in a state which they later identify as pleasure, joy, or ecstasy? The second question might be "Is it enlightened or escapist to seek and enjoy such intense pleasure?" Finally, "Do mystical or religious experiences really signify holy contact, or just mental disconnection?"

Chemicals for Courage: The Rapid Response System

The first question is the easiest to deal with in terms of general brain biochemistry and it was previewed in some detail in Chapter Seven. From the molecular viewpoint, we are doing it with adrenalin, ACTH, serotonin, dopamine, and a few other brain chemicals. The recipe differs from location to location, but nearly all physiological and perceptual effects of a state of bliss can be directly or indirectly associated with the effects of these hormones and neurotransmitters on some organ or brain structure itself.

Adrenalin is a master hormone of the human body; it is our natural metabolic catalyst that can in turn affect the release of numerous other compounds which can have a dramatic effect on the brain and the body.

It is manufactured in the adrenal cortex, a clump of chromaffin cells located at the top of the kidney. As "kidney" in Latin is *rena, ad-renal-in* simply describes where it's made, "from over the kidneys," a handy place to get it into the bloodstream. The adrenal cortex is a little local chemical plant with wires up to the brain. Like a personal turbocharger, occasional adrenalin is normal, but too much can exhaust or impair us. Many of us are aware that highly adrenergic states, if not tempered, lead to stress and anxiety, high blood pressure, drug and alcohol abuse, and impairment of the immune response.

On the other hand, as adrenalin is a better stimulant than any drug yet devised it might have been expected that we would work out ways to get a little more here and there. Bears don't mind a few bee stings if they can get to the honey, and humans have always been looking for various ways to unwrap themselves from their overly personalized, solitary minds even if some of the techniques are not only daring, but dangerous. It seems that we learned how to manipulate our endocrine system some time ago to produce these intense consciousness-altering experiences. It has to do with how internal brain activity causes hormonal happies and how some stone-age shamans broke the code ages ago, probably by mistake. We unconsciously learned how to manipulate our own neural systems to create experiences guaranteed to spice up consciousness and anchor us more realistically in the present.

An easy way to unload the adrenal cortex is to create a sudden increase in brain activity. This would indicate that something either very familiar or very threatening were happening "out there" which might require sudden extra energy or strength. One chemical trip signal is a rapid rise in the uptake of the neurotransmitter norepinephrine. Epinephrine is simply Greek for adrenalin; in Greek *epi* means over, and *nephron* means kidney. However, since "epinephrine" sounds much more scholarly than "adrenalin," noradrenalin became norepinephrine; the "substance preceding adrenalin."

Norepinephrine is found in much of the neocortex, where most of our recently evolved brain mass is located. When norepinephrine is suddenly all over the place, it's like yelling "fire!" down the wires and the adrenal cortex obligingly dumps the adrenalin into our bloodstream without asking what's happening. Usually there isn't time to ask, which is why it has to be so automatic. The speed with which this electrochemical circuit can fire off is remarkable. It is, after all, our emergency getaway system; designed for instant deployment in life-threatening scenarios.

On a given day, for instance, we are walking down the street. Our body is operating well within its limits, our senses picking up the information and processing it at normal brain speed. We are in regular day-to-day consciousness with perception smoothly guiding us through our time and space. Then suddenly it happens. It doesn't matter what happens, it just has to be sudden enough to create a sudden surge of norepinephrine. In this instance, our pleasant stroll is suddenly interrupted by the squeal of brakes shrieking into our auditory cortex together with an exploding image on our retinas of an out of control car skidding into the intersection just ahead of us.

As the information from the eyes and ears hits the top level of the brain, neurons race to compute escape trajectories. There is a mild biochemical eruption at the higher cortical levels as cells careen into overload for a microsecond. The sudden flood of norepinephrine into synapses interrupts the lazy spontaneous firing of resting neurons, opening the gates for the sensory information pulsing in from outside. Neural circuits flash-energize like neon signs, extending in a crackling frenzy faster than thought as patterns and networks start interconnecting all over like a regular fireworks finale. The instant chain reaction shifts the entire brain into electrochemical excess.

This is your primeval tiger racing across the savannah; this is the only "is" that is and the only word of God is Get-Out-Now! In less than a tenth of a second, the surge hits the adrenal cortex, completely bypassing the brain's interpretive centers. The adrenalin unloads directly into the bloodstream, rushing up the arteries to a brain that is only a heartbeat away. Like gasoline dumped on a blaze, it hits the frantically firing neurons, energizing both hemispheres for a massive reaction.

Instantly the visual cortex at the back of the brain swings into power overdrive, neurons firing away at triple speed like a movie camera suddenly cranked up to the max. This is how both film makers and brains create slow motion visuals, that almost miraculous sense of "time standing still" when we really need a miracle to get us out of harm's way. With the brain on fast, and our world in slow motion, all the smooth muscle in the body is contracting at once. Hairs snap straight up in their follicles, the diaphragm contracts in a gasp, and all the blood vessels give a squeeze, sending a surge of blood towards our liver and a shiver through our body. We are now in a state about as close to the Sanskrit *samadhi*, direct contact with ultimate reality, as we will ever be but there's no time to reflect on it now.

Less than half a second has passed; already the liver is jettisoning its rich supply of glucose into the blood, charging it and fueling the muscles for powerful and immediate action. The body sweeps through biochemical transformations faster than the mind can think in sequence, slamming molecules into position, wrenching the spine straight, pulling time itself to bits as life and death hold fast for a moment while we yank ourselves out of danger in the nick of time. In the full adrenalin shock of trauma or terror, mothers have lifted cars off children, hunters leapt to impossibly high branches, and cripples walked with broken legs. Adrenalin is our shock-action hormone; if it kept on coming we would drop from burn-out and exhaustion. Under circumstances such as these it's hard to recognize a pleasure circuit when we see it. Getting our pants scared off is not anybody's idea of ecstasy, especially when it's real danger. Excitement, perhaps but hardly rapture in recognizable form.

If the car skids out of the intersection, or if it turns out to be just some kid laying rubber for kicks, the hormones taper off immediately. The smooth muscle in the body now relaxes, with predictable results. The cold shiver is replaced with a warm rush as the blood returns to the extremities. At this point the bladder or bowel may fail if their sphincters relax too much; a not uncommon occurrence during a terrifying experience. There is a warm hormonal tingle throughout the body and the mind is still in a fuzz as the brain recovers cognition in a foggy biochemical afterglow. It will take some time to cool down, synchronize the parts and restart the clock-time sequencer to regain measured, rational, comparative thought again. We were yanked beyond our limits, and returned to this life alive. There are always artifacts as well: brilliantly remembered moments when we were so much a part of the world around us that we were nearly out of our minds and lived to talk about it. If we had been lost in our personal virtual chronology up to that moment, it was a sudden drop kick into present tense perception with the volume up to twelve. A full-strength adrenalin rush will always put a new card in our files. The future will never be quite the same.

Humans may go through this a lot more often than other primates because of what happened during the last two million years as our brains evolved and enlarged. In species time it usually takes a long time for adaptive changes to take place, for a nose to evolve to a trunk for instance. Evolution may occur by fits and starts but it does not happen quickly; genetic manipulation is involved and humans take at least fourteen years to recycle a set. The concept of redesigning a whole nervous system, our entire hormonal checks-and-balances operation, with a million year deadline is just not feasible unless we're all creationists. Traditionally, interrelated systems change together. It would be hard to imagine talking, for instance, if our tongues expanded their mass fourfold without some extensive dental work and a complete jaw retrofit. Still, we managed to quadruple the volume of the brain in less than two million years.

Our hormonal systems originally operated with the standard 300 cubic centimeter brain that guides the average primate. Within only two million years, however, we managed to upgrade the old 300 cc clunker to our mega-memory, parallel processing, pattern sequencing, 1,200 cc electrochemical powerhouse. It was like bolting a 1,200 cc Harley Davidson motorcycle engine to a skateboard. The endocrine system had been accustomed for many millions of years to take orders from less than a quarter the number of neurons we now have howling "wolf" or "wonderful" when anything pops up on the screen bigger than bite size. We can get excited by nearly anything if we set up our hair-trigger human consciousness with enough repeated stimulation.

This is not to suggest that packing on that last 1,000 cubic centimeters of virtual memory and processing capacity was a bad thing. With the added thousand cubic centimeters, we gained time, space, imagination, and conscious perception, but our brain still operates by electrochemistry and our endocrine system is still getting wagged by the brain. From an information point of view, our greater neural mass is just more processing power and virtual memory. From an electrochemical point of view, however, four times the amount of biochemical turnover can be created for the same amount of stimulation. The entire spectrum is shifted.

And it wasn't just the higher cortical centers that grew. The fine-movement controlling cerebellum gained proportionately just as much mass. This was important because fine tuned sequential muscle response is what lets apes and monkeys navigate about in the treetops. Once again, humans ended up with nearly four times more. The media-forebrain bundle grew to transfer subtle pre-frontal motivational data directly to the brain stem itself; humans can intend to do it right the next time.

Our moves are much more mindful. Many brutes have more brute strength than we, but humans are the smoothest on earth at any learned form of muscular coordination. Cats couldn't dance if they wanted to.

Our greatly expanded neural mass provided the basis to create neural networks which grew by degree deeper and more detailed. The primate forebrain, which sequences exquisitely timed muscular movements with a precision unparalleled in the animal kingdom, evolved until muscle pattern sequencing was yanking huge patterns through intricate maneuvers, spilling off abstractions in a continuing unconscious cascade. As our Cro-Magnon ancestors developed this sequencing into abstracts and transforms, we were also perfecting conscious recall. Soon the recollection of the seasons woke us to the cyclic nature of the world around us. We began to predict, to prepare, and do the one thing that nature never does and never can do. We learned to repeat on purpose. It was the beginning of our control over our environment, our control over our destiny and our evolution as a species. We learned when to sow the fields, how to predict the glaze on a pot, how to plot macro-economic curves on graphs. The world outside will never do it again the same way, but we learned to repeat things first for mastery, and later just for fun.

This is only possible because mental activity always leaves its traces. Each time a thought or a muscular activity is repeated, patterns will extend. Our neural networks grow each time we repeat, making us more sensitive to the expected while paying less attention to the formless or the incidental. Our cognition soon becomes proactive as we begin to invest meaning into whatever we know the most and we begin to re-shape the world into a mirror of our likes and dislikes. It is the beginning of personality and force of habit, of the thoughtless repetition that the East calls Samsara, and the West calls ego. Our neural nets grow even as we sleep. Familiar networks extend as random pulses wander through them even while we dream.

This constant activity and change is what makes it impossible to compare the brain and any sort of computer. The patterns of recognition in the brain are not pictures or even diagrams, they may be very subtle ripple formations in the constant coursing electrochemical currents circulating at every moment. Like a quantum flash of time that theoretically locates an electron in a cloud of probabilities, the picture of brain patterns changing and shifting through the physical channels and chemical bridges is discernable only to quantum impulse in an otherwise chaotic mass of streaming activity. It is theoretically possible, but beyond human understanding at this time. We can only imagine that which our mind can focus, and these things are beyond the focussing resolution of the only consciousness we have.

Repetition of familiar activities or thought patterns eventually so extend and interconnect interneuronal networks that familiar stimulation can awaken a very large associative network of cells. At any time past the age of about three, we are generating a great number of these networks. Many neurons are often on the edge of response simply from the stimulation of internal chatter, and are easily pushed into heightened activity by a good dose of external perception. Consequentially, in humans, the synergy between a large and energetic associative neural network and the input of inherently familiar information can easily create enough brain activity to nudge the adrenal cortex into action even when little may be happening out there in the non-virtual real world.

An example of this effect, mentioned in chapter seven, was the sudden and unexpected face of a long-missed loved one in a crowd. Facial recognition is quicker in women than in men, but either way visual data shoots down the media-forebrain bundle shortcut directly to the limbic system, the basic structure which links memories and emotions. We judge reality by emotional clues, and the limbic system acts as the immune-response of our personal consciousness, our constant personal virtual reality check. Before cognitive processing even starts, familiar patterns in the hippocampus are already responding in recognition.

This basic level of recognition can itself produce quite a surge of emotional reaction even before we start up our cognitive search-and-compare processes. The hippocampus is an ancient part of the mammal brain evolved directly from the olfactory bulb and our emotions are easily aroused by familiar scents. In fact, smell recognition completely bypasses the brain's fine-tuning reality filter, the reticular activating system, hitting so hard that it often surprises us when an unexpected scent revives a vivid rush of emotional memories.

Even basic structures cannot be subjected to constant excitement, however. If the hippocampus is overstimulated for too long, its cellular mechanisms will start to fault out. If things get too excessive, in other words, it loses control and the system can disinhibit. If this happens, our virtual reality, our sense of the world and its meaning will destabilize. As the limbic system defines our reality by denying emotional existence to all but parts of our moment to moment perception, it also provides the boundaries between thought and belief. It is limbic system distortions, along with suspension loss of chronological time, that create most of the altered perceptions of dreams, delusions, and death. Reality may start in a part of the brain as old as the hills, but it's not hard to hot-wire the system and light up the sky.

Returning to the face in the crowd, when the visual image hits we suddenly recognize a face we know so well. If there is a large amount of familiarity to any perception, the hippocampal response starts a biochemical cascade effect identical to when we thought we might get hit by the car. The clock speed of human consciousness, dependent on many sequential electrochemical activities already discussed at length, is so awfully slow that anything as basic as recognition appears instantaneous to us. The appearance of a lost loved one can have the same hormonal impact on our brain as the image of the car skidding into the intersection, only this time there's clearly no danger.

That much is obvious to our senses, which are being intensified, amplified, and nearly overruled by the powerful effects of an internal pattern-recognition cascade. With so many associative memories, large and complex networked patterns energize instantly, creating a norepinephrine surge. Naturally, out rushes adrenalin willy-nilly. When we trip the circuit with internal familiarity rather than danger, we call the hormonal jolt "joy." Now the gasp, the shiver, and the warm rush are magical. The sense of time slowed down can be dreamlike, not nightmarish. It's exactly the same molecules, but this time we did it to ourselves by energizing lowered resistance networks all over the place. It impacts dramatically, adding life to our time and space, taking us out of our thoughts and into the world that exists around us.

Since the majority of our memories are in an unconscious state most of the time, we are all subject to specific and personal hormonal responses to many old embedded and forgotten patterns. If they are memories we treasure, recollection and thought intensify and further personalize our responses. One very interesting feature of this ability to amplify experience with memory, creating pleasurable hormonal "rewards," is how we inadvertently and largely unconsciously learn how to utilize this capacity to help us get our bearings in life. The massive mind we depend on for everything operates us within a virtual reality and if we can't dump personal ego occasionally, we can begin to believe our internal world is the only one there is.

The buildup of personal habits makes us always more repetitious and insensitive to the changing world around us. How, then, could we get a better look at the present moment to see it as it really is, rather than so distorted with our recollection and expectation? How do we get a really fresh look at it all? Why, simply let loose the hormones and shoot into psychosensual overdrive for a moment. If we energize enough of our internal associative memory, we can amplify any experience. Then, with only limited amounts of external involvement we can have all manner of meaningful excitement right between our own ears.

Associative avalanching can trigger major hormone releases in people for reasons ranging from romance to scholarship, from a celebrity on the stage to a cockroach in the kitchen. The human mind has harnessed the world to our whims, but individually it can propel us into some of the most inane sorts of behaviors. With age, we only become more specific. Teenagers swoon *en masse* at the same pop stars while adults, having grown more personal, have more specific heroes in their own larger but specialized fields of association. Cultural holidays and family events can be guaranteed to evoke strong feelings in us all no matter what our race or nationality. Our most basic memories, the earliest ones, are the ones that unite us all. We all feel them the same way. Heart to heart, all human minds are very similar.

We all seek excitement because it is the necessary and repeated meeting with our hormonal clues, forcing our feelings to their natural limits, that alone can keep us defined and alert in a world we have made much too safe for such a curious little ape. Sometimes the trip circuit is unconsciously planned into our work routine, such as never allowing enough time and getting caught in exciting panic deadlines much too often. Some hobbies, sports, and occupations are clearly going to include more thrills than others; police officers, drug dealers, and rock stars wouldn't do it if it didn't excite them. The official company slogan of rock-climbing outfitter Yvon Chouinard is simply "Let's Go Get Scared." Nobody ever lost money with a good rollercoaster. Still, most of our personal routines and repetitions are not unpleasant, and we get our hormonal happies less dramatically through varying forms of exercise, entertainment, or familiar ritual, be they domestic, cultural, or religious.

There is a darker side to all of this, however. The more we repeat anything at all, the more familiarity it will have, and the more we will tend to
further repetition. Survival is the only thing the brain was evolved for,
and anything that happened which we survived is better than the unknown. This means that anything from daily habits to self-destructive
relationships can, and will, through repetition eventually become self-re-
generating patterns. Soon, they are altering our course through life like
the invisible attractions of large planets, massive with our accumulated
past, able to pull us again and again into the old familiar orbits without
our conscious will or even realization.

By the time we've lived a number of years we begin to repeat by unconscious habit those very activities which were once quite coincidental
simply because they make us comfortable. Our walls are being erected
without a lot of noise, leaving us emotionally with a rather limited space
in which to exercise the full spectrum of our powerful systems of perception, thought, and action. Rarely if ever facing real life-threatening or
life-enhancing situations, we become dependent instead on dependable
emotional triggers like a rat in a cage twiddling the button for safe little
jolts to help forget some primal urge to get out and raid a grain sack in
the real world outside.

We are heading into the world of synthetic challenges, wins, and
losses; an existence of futile repetition, circling in Samsara, a self-cen-
tered life rich with predictable pleasures. At the same time, even our
most painfully unpleasant attention-getters are eventually woven in as
part of the repeating and self-fulfilling scenario. "Honest" expressions of
anger become repetitious ritual conflicts against the same old adver-
saries; infatuation or excitement can be honed by compulsive attention to
any person or activity. When human inventiveness in prediction and
planning begins to be used mainly to arrange personal repertories of the
same loves, the same hates, the same fights, and the same triumphs, it's
hard to explain it. As a result, we will often go to great lengths to create
and articulate personal, cultural, and even national myths to justify
repertories of the same old patterns of expectation, pleasure, disappointment, and rage; the human hormonal four-step that we mistake for the
harmony of life.

High Technology and Gridlocked Minds: A Twentieth Century Limit

Helping us along in this universal trend to replace perception with predictable thrills is the enormous amount of sophisticated technology currently employed to create and promote those events which are supposed to excite us. At this time, the manufacture of vicarious realities, professional sports, movie stars, star wars, drug wars, news bites, super heroes, and sitcoms is a multi-multi-billion dollar industry. As soon as our modern civilization saved us from being faced with real danger it seems that it started being used to spice our lives with ritual romance, drama, and mock involvements to save us from terminal boredom. Julius Caesar, asked how he kept the Romans pacified, replied "Bread and circuses": processed food and cheap thrills. There is nothing new here; we've simply brought the Coliseum into our lives so that mayhem for the masses is more profitable.

Since so many of us have little meaningful involvement with our technical 20th century world, we have developed this unconscious itch for some sort of deeper meaning. To many, this simply translates to anything that seems to get us excited. By the 1990s, advances in broadcast communications had reduced much of the developed world nearly to the level of a popular mediacracy. Policy is formed by politicians elected in response to the way they are perceived in the media as responding to supposed dangers. As wars are the best way to get the fear hormones running, to win elections, wars have to be declared every year or so on foes as unlikely as Grenada or Panama, as well as on every domestic problem from pot holes to pot. It is no mistake that presidents Reagan and Bush chose war over peace both internationally and internally. Excitement always sells.

Dealing with everyday life challenges just doesn't seem exciting enough in a world filled with individuals who don't know why they're so anxious and don't know whom to blame. The current solution is to treat life like television, quickly abandoning anything unexciting or boring like changing a channel. The networks claim to have only four money makers, "the four C's": Cops, Crime, Courts, and Comedy. Even the news is not news, but a search for whatever plays best to the most basic emotions, slanted and edited with specific attention to the sensational.

In one famous NBC memo, it was made clear that "news" should never be shown as it is, but always packaged as little mini-dramas. We are mainly being informed by thespian newscasters whose packaged candor and pancake sincerity has reached new heights of hypocrisy and manipulation, showing us only what boosts network ratings as our minds slowly turn to mush and mayhem. In 1993, veteran newscaster Dan Rather said aloud what many had been thinking.

The problem? "Our bosses. They aren't venal, they're afraid of ratings slippages. They've got us putting more and more fuzz and wuzz on their air, cop show stuff, so as to compete not with other news programs but with entertainment programs—including those posing as news programs—for bodies, mayhem, and lurid tales. We trivialize important subjects. We put videotape through a Cuisinart to come up with high speed MTV-style cross cuts. And just to cover our asses, we give the best slots to gossip and prurience. We should all be ashamed of what we have done." Between politicians who need wars and international media conglomerates who need viewers, we are getting a very warped, very violent and very destructive view of reality from all sides. Day after day passive minds gorge on this fantasy and violence, which escalates in direct proportion to the hours of coverage it gets. Nothing sells like thrills, and so it continues day in and day out, pleasure pats from the media priests of a processed, amplified, and endlessly promoted exciting electroreality.

Those who suffer the most, as in any wars, are the children. As more and more two career parents let infant children between the ages of one and three watch television for long periods of time, their brains are pickled by the ratings and their reality becomes permanently warped. At the American Academy of Pediatrics annual meeting in 1991, Marvin O. Kolb moderated a panel on children and television violence. "To kids, everything looks real and with cumulative exposure there is an increasing tendency to see violence as the norm," he remarked, echoed by pediatrician Victor Strasburger of the University of New Mexico, Albuquerque. "If they see a good guy killing a bad guy, they begin to think that this is an O.K. way to resolve problems."

For some reason the United States government has taken years to note the clear linkage between violence in media entertainment, foreign policy, and American society. A truly frightening study was presented in 1991 at the meeting of the American Psychiatric Association by psychiatrist and epidemiologist Brian Centerwall. Centerwall studied the crime rates in the United States, Canada, and South Africa. He discovered that crime rates began to rise about five to seven years after television was introduced, as soon as the first generation of exposed kids start turning dramatic television shows into real life.

Television was introduced to the United States and Canada in the 1950's but didn't get to South Africa until 1965. In testing his hypothesis, Centerwall predicted that white South African murder rates would remain stable while U.S. and Canadian rates were rising in the late 50's and early 60's, and then start to rise in the early 80's. That is exactly what happened. The pattern he discovered, rise in crime within five to seven years and a doubling within fifteen to twenty, has since been born out in every regional, racial, and international comparison he has made, and for every violent crime including murder, rape, and assault.

"If you knew when a region acquired television, you could predict with considerable accuracy when the homicide rate would increase. It's a very tight relationship," he explained. Other possible causes such as civil rights activities, urbanization, and alcohol abuse didn't fit the data. "If the technology of television had never been developed," Centerwall concluded, "There would be about 10,000 fewer dead people in the United States each year." Despairing at the violence and misery in the lives of her teen-age patients, Dr. Barbara Staggers, Director of the adolescent medicine clinic at the Oakland Children's Hospital in California, also set the blame on the constant glorification of violence and suggestive glamour. "Everything they see is guns and sex, guns and sex," she explained pointing out that in 1991 homicide was the No. 2 cause of death among young people aged 15 to 19, with suicide No. 3.

Violence sells, but it kills. In 1992, Colombia began censoring television for violence; a year later the United States held congressional hearings to try to find ways to control it. Still, it may be too late for many. By now, entire generations are being molded not by history, but by edited media versions of it. Past events are no longer actual events, but dramatizations. "We live in a media age," says film critic Leonard Malkin, "If a television or theatrical movie can paint a vivid enough picture for young people, they'll believe that's the way it was." We are gradually losing touch with reality and wondering why even as we tune in for more. The National Council of Churches avoided outright calls for censorship, but went on record. "We strongly object, however, to what we see as misuse of the First Amendment, by commercial interests, as a cover of a quest for profit." "If you have 30 seconds glamorizing soap you sell soap," explained U.S. Senator Paul Simon, "And if you have 25 minutes of glamorizing violence, you have violence."

Our inability to enjoy the simple congeniality of a so-called normal existence, paradise for any lower creature, can be blamed nearly entirely on the private media, reaping fortunes while force feeding our senses a deadening diet of danger and drama. As a result, the real world dulls. We begin to use it mainly as a staging ground for dreams and fantasies, constructions we weave from synthetic hopes and popular fears and carry about in our minds, helping us to create a world as two-dimensional as any soap opera, docu-drama, or MTV video.

Eventually, self-generated cycles of predictable thrills and chills can build such barriers that even instances of real human drama, tragedy or joy lose their power to teach or guide. It would be naive, of course, to expect that one or two full-tilt hormonal rushes could unknot a mental harness perfected by years of habit. We are more easily temporarily illuminated than fully enlightened and the glow usually dies away. Those rapidly converted are often rapidly unconverted as the much deeper and more personal tides of personal repetition wash away at recent experience. We fall back into comfortable and familiar patterns of our virtual joys and synthetic fears, punctuating and perpetuating our oscillations in a world of echoes and dreams. We learn to avoid activities with personal implications; people or experiences we cannot fit into our predictable world. Our neural nets, there to save us from need, grow untended like kudzu across our internal landscapes until we are mentally strangled in tangles of vain illusion and imaginary fears.

These days we have developed ever more novel ways to shield our senses from the present moment and be further led by our own noses, never having to react to reality. We have everything from Walkmans to Winfreys to hide us, and guide us, and give us familiar mental cud to chew until we wish for no more. Many of us become completely satisfied with a nearly total avoidance of the uneven experience of life, replacing it with routines as easy to maintain as the rat's pleasure button.

Subtly at first, and with greater regularity as we become habit-ridden, our emotions become stunted and ritualized. We become as self engrossed in our self-created sideshow as any video game or computer addict hunched over his electronic toy, flashing and beeping in a dark arcade. Like rapturous rodents with a wire up the brain, we turn increasingly to well rehearsed, reliable forms of self-stimulation, pushing the buttons again and again, eyes turned inward to our whirling fantasies, waiting for the jackpot we have learned to fashion from our own mental substance until we are eaten up in our minds. We become trapped in our own virtual reality with virtually no way out.

As our natural tendency to follow past experience through future expectations into various mind-deadening states of mental gridlock seems to be unavoidable with an accumulative memory, it is no wonder that we seek an escape. Our temporary solutions are to shock the mind into a state of thoughtlessness with the help of various social substances, excessive sensuality, and thrilling ritual. These will always be available. If there were any permanent solutions, however, or at least some practical methods for a thoughtful dip into the present tense without self-denying or self destructive behavior, it would seem whoever has them should step up and tell us about them. Actually, people have been doing that for ages. We call them saints and saviors, and we call their suggestions "wisdom."

Can we cleanse the brain of its accumulation of outdated pasts and one-sided futures without getting brainwashed in the process? Can we straighten out the tangles in our neural nets we created ourselves, those cycles that keep sending us in circles, without losing our bearings or our brains? In fact, it is not only possible, but numerous ways to achieve this end have been taught and practiced throughout history as spiritual instruction, mental training, personal skills, and even more powerfully embodied within the most fundamental rituals of traditional religious practice wherever it is found.

Part Four:
The Future

9

Priests and Prophets

Fulfillment in Real Time

The methods we use to find both our freedom and our fulfillment are clever in theory and often elegant in execution. The purpose is still to generalize personality temporarily, to neutralize the virtual ego and attempt to consciously experience our perception from a different perspective, without our self-created filters. Fortunately, we don't have to do anything violent at all; all we have to do is to overdrive the time sequencer and we'll drop ego just like that. If we can create a non-synchronous consciousness we can't do future transforms or abstracts or anything. We are forced into the actuality of wherever we are at the moment.

At any moment, our reality is anchored into the neural nets of our memory and expectation. Cognitive thought can work only in chronological time because we think comparatively. We compare ourselves against outside situations as well as inner projections to gain our self-image, and this requires the ability to scan patterns, sequence, and compare. If we lost that ability, our situation would become incomparable. With our cognitive centers off-line, we would be thinking with our hippocampus; pure emotive perception with no space-time limitations. This certainly comes close to Godhead, but it is also perilously close to nowhere.

Whatever it is, it is certainly outside the Aristotelian mindset of "Know Thyself" and "Nothing in Excess." In our own virtual world of time and space, we normally need one to perceive the other. When our sense of time checks out, the self goes with it and we get a chance to experience life from a truly universal, unlimited perspective. In asynchronous perception, we always forget ourselves. If we could keep our mind in that place for a moment we would actually, finally, be in synchrony with the rest of the universe without the shadings and burdens of personal hopes or fears. This is no state of mind for doing the taxes or even crossing the street but it is superlative for a sudden shift into the immediate moment, an excitingly direct interface with the real world. It is considered a form of higher consciousness in the East, where getting totally outside the personal context is considered the goal of all human spiritual endeavor. So how do we do this?

Fortunately, we don't have to unplug the brain and pull out memory chips. Chaotic quantum pattern memories aren't built like that, and the techniques we use are quite different. In our case, the easiest thing to do is to create "I-O" or "Input-Output" faults. In computers, this means that data input speed and output speed are out of synchrony. Just as time distortions occur when the brain speeds up, there are ways to create even deeper experiences if we force consciousness into other places through self-induced biochemical gymnastics. In the brain, these planned electrochemical anomalies can lead to states of consciousness ranging from mild hormonal highs to complete adrenergic paralysis; from delight, to amazement, to ecstacy.

Planned Satisfaction: Stretching the Nets

The interconnected nature of the brain seems to guarantee that associative memory networks would be interlinked throughout many different structures, looping through discrete areas handling different tasks. One good way to unhinge memory, then, would be to overstimulate certain parts of the system with hormones and unbalance normal brain activity. We can selectively knock out parts of cognitive process by exhausting our neurons until they simply can't react properly. If we could trick our brain into doing this, large networked patterns stretching throughout the brain could be temporarily unravelled as the input-output needs of one part of the system were shifted out of synchrony with other parts. The detail of the holographic quantum patterns could easily drop by a factor or so. Ego would slide out of focus without losing focus.

For instance, if we overstimulate and disrupt functions in the higher cortical areas, we might "crash" our perception into a lower-brain backup, a form of low-definition consciousness. This would drop us back into something much closer to instinctual sensibility for a short time. We would be unthinking, and yet aware. This highly charged form of selfless perception would be experienced as a state of grace to a religious Westerner, samadhi or satori to a Hindu or Buddhist. It's the same place, a self-induced state of higher consciousness, lower consciousness in fact, and we all have the ability to do it. In fact, we've all done it many times.

The usual method is to create huge synthetic patterns in the brain through attention to planned activities which are largely repetitious. In this way, we can be sure that there will eventually be enough associative neural networking to trigger a hormonal response. Since adrenalin release will speed up parts of the brain while intense repetition will exhaust other parts, if we keep both of them up long enough our comparative perception will occasionally fault out as input-output faults begin to appear at various levels of cortical structure.

Eventually, repetition of any complex activity can trigger enough response for mild hormonal body highs, pleasant mental and emotional stimulation without either fantasy or a lot of frustration. It's not a virtual event, it's a real world experience and the added hormonal surge greatly heightens our experiential perception. Creating such large networks takes time, however. Unless we are into Eastern meditative practices or artistic obsession, we are not by nature very good at nearly perfect thought repetition. In fact the way most of us achieve these states has the advantage of ganging differing brain areas together for an effective overkill. We can do this with any mind/body activity which requires thoughtful practice; from music, to jogging, to drama, to dance.

The recent ability of our forebrain to sequence complex patterns of muscular movement evolved, in humans, into our ability to derive abstractions and predictions through sequential comparison of the huge patterns themselves. We will cross-connect all sorts of neural networks if we repeat any careful activity over and over again. The constant repetition involved in the mastery of any skill occurs as we repeat until we achieve a desired level of competence, an image we project in our own mind. As mastery requires practice, it will inevitably lead to emotionally charged experiences. Soon, we learn to enjoy the "feeling" of confidence in our ability, our craft, and our art.

As each repetition occurs in a different time frame, a new pattern is perceived by our senses at that moment. After a period of time, these routines create immense and extended patterns linked throughout higher brain centers that routinely handle our perceptive and cognitive tasks. The engaging of different brain centers in any attentive, repetitious practice will eventually interconnect enough associative memory that chance resonance between these internal super-nets and external conditions can occasionally trigger a powerful hormonal response. Unlike our mental gridlock patterns, our unconscious habits we repeat and then try to justify, these are patterns which we created with conscious attention and full knowledge of what we were doing. The feeling is often described as enthusiasm; again from the Greek *en theos*, a feeling that God is smiling on you.

This is how artists and athletes, every craftsperson and every musician, and anyone else who has experienced the personal glow of a job well done gets those thrills. When our skill and the circumstance combine just right, we lose ourselves in the moment. These moments of mild ego loss are instructive, not destructive, because they were done purposefully. What makes the experience particularly nice is that it often happens when we really are doing our best and in the presence of friends or even admirers.

There are hours of dues to pay, of course, as we set up those deep patterns during days of mindful repetition. The long hours practicing scales, the steps of dance, the slap-shots that slip and the dunks that don't, all are part of this patient assembly of those mental patterns which will let us lose our fears without losing ourselves. Over time, amateurism becomes expertise. The body begins to move in smooth curves of carefully controlled energy, the fingers find the frets without a doubt, the colors hold, the dancer's body wakes, and the energy begins to flow from within. Sooner or later, the experience must happen. Practice and action are finally in tune, and it's puck into the net, ball over the goalposts, and the moments all musicians know when the music takes over, sweeping them into harmonies as mind and body forsake time and space in the glow we know so well.

This is the feeling of being totally in the flow of life, the Tao, the dharma, in God's kingdom, blessed and grateful to simply be. It is finding the Holy Spirit alive and well, the childlike world before self and beyond ego, not outer space, but another space. It is the living, exciting, full experience of life itself, unapart and reassuring, up front and right now.

To a certain extent, then, every time that we repeat thoughtfully something that we love to do, we add to our growing networks of associative energy. Then, when outside events energize them within the right setting, we may find ourselves experiencing a very pleasant hormonal whole body glow, accompanied by partial ego loss in supportive and protective surroundings. The more brain area which can be called into resonance, the stronger the feelings; it takes a lot longer if we just watch. A full involvement in life and the things we love to do make it easier.

When we lose ourselve in our music, art, hobbies, studies, athletic contests, professions, personal fitness, volunteer activities; even cooking, working, and parenting, it always pulls us out of our virtual reality and makes us a part of a bigger pattern. As the joys of personal fulfillment always require practice, it's important to find a practice that we can enjoy. If paying the dues is a pleasure in and of itself, the payoff will come sooner, and be even more pleasurable.

Priests and Prophets: Showing the Way

There are, moreover, even higher power versions of these methods of finding an eternal moment and the peaceful heart. Once again, the basic technique is the same, but with added subroutines which tend to act as catalytic boosters. Like fine tuning a combustion engine, these added mind exercises may kick in at just the right time, adding such direction and power to the experience that the effects can last for days, months, or longer.

In a Christian, Muslim and Jewish setting, these experiences are associated with religious rapture. The Hindu might define it as shaktipat, while Zen Buddhists speak of satori. The emotional experience is sudden insight combined with childlike wonder; unaware of the self, but very aware of being; the infant at the threshold of knowing. When these experiences occur within the focus of a regular symbolic or physical practice they can easily provide deep experiences of brimming happiness, a pure personal fulfillment both powerful and indescribable.

In fact, the only time that we could be so purely fulfilled was at a very young and tender age. As infants, we were the center of the universe; everything was done for us and because of us. There will never be again a time of the sure and undifferentiated self which we knew as very young children. Comparative cognitive consciousness won't even operate until the systems architecture is solid; we spent a long time in a place where time didn't count for much and where we were the only soul that mattered. Like Adam and Eve, we assumed that we had the only Eden in town. Without the accumulation of memory to crowd our sureness with caution or regret, time was always now. This universal time of early innocence is, in that sense, also a time of profound self-knowledge. It is our human misfortune that this particular form of perception is nearly impossible to recapture or reproduce in the mature human brain. Even if we were to recapture it, we could only use it for the experience itself. Non-comparative, asynchronous thought may be the experience of being in a sureness we have sought ever since, but it is what it is, an immature and unorganized form of our precise and measured consciousness, a baby's view from an infant brain. Still, it was the last time our mind was at one with our world, and we need the reminders.

To shake hands with our soul, then, that part in each of us that does not think, but knows who and what we are, all we have to do is to recreate a nearly infantile brain state and have a reunion with ourselves beyond comparison, before good and bad, before right and wrong. We just "were" in those endless days and we didn't worry much about it. It had been that way forever. If we want to find ourselves, this is the way to go, but it is not a transcendant move upward. It is a return to another reality, the one that we knew before we knew anything else. "Let the little children come unto me," said Jesus, "hinder them not, for unto them belong the kingdom of heaven." Jesus didn't have kids himself, but he knew.

To do an ego evaporation into a state of grace, we must do more than create some I-O faults with hormones and planned neural saturation. We may have to put the entire brain into biochemical exhaustion. Only through deep and massive disruption of the circuitry of the brain will multiple parts of consciousness fault out at the same time, creating for a moment a cohesive, but much more basic universe, a place beyond human consciousness. If we can know for a moment that reunion with *chairos*, we can know oneness.

This is to experience the love of God; to reach Nirvana or even Brahman, a vantage point so far beyond cognitive perception that the earliest and simplest patterns behind the nets and networks of thought become momentarily sensible as the mind sinks back into a primeval state and we are reacquainted with the shared and simple consciousness of our own infancy. We were all gods then; and as Moses, Jesus, Mohammed, Buddha, Mahavira, Manu, Lao Tzu, Confucius and all the great teachers have said, we can be just as holy now. We just have to regain that fearless, innocent perspective and we can find ourselves again at any age.

To accomplish this, we have to affect a lot more brain mass and the most interesting difference in method is that the repetitive activities need not initially be meaningful. In fact, it is often better if they originally seem meaningless. If they are meaningless initially, the practices will become through repetition alone meaningful in and of themselves. If enough of the brain is eventually associated into massive synthetic networks, should a hormonal surge hit, the entire cognitive mind can short out. This would leave consciousness in limbic system limbo and produce everything from out of body perceptions to rapturous experiences, from dreamlike scenarios to superhuman exertions.

The aspect of neural behavior which makes this possible is that we can, by simple repetition alone, exhaust entire layers of consciousness by repeating the same stimulation over and over, just as vision will blur after staring at the same object for too long. If the brain is prepared by a combination of multiple repetitions in enough locations, the energy in a large, synthetic associative network may build up high enough that just one more stress can collapse parts of the normal thinking process. The neurons just stop firing for a moment to get a rest.

If this happens, the informational overload may be automatically shunted downward to a more basic level, which itself may have been similarly overstimulated. Like a domino effect, the cascade alerts the adrenal cortex and the released hormones will hit a hair-trigger, exhausted brain. If the resulting overstimulation exhausts the limbic system as well, our entire sense of self can melt momentarily in a powerful mental experience analogous to being dissolved into a timeless moment and reborn again.

Getting there requires mindful and attentive physical action which is repeated over and over, only this time it is not in furtherance of any personal goals. It is ritualistic and recognized as such. The fingers move rosary beads for the devotees of Mary, Krishna, and Tara; the mind directs faithful hands to fold, or move, or to hold. The Muslim bows to Mecca in a precise formula, hands out, hands down. There may be familiar music. Familiar scents, such as incense, will excite the olfactory cortex. There may be ceremonial swaying, walking, kneeling, ritual hand movements, ritual dance, or prostrations. Shakers danced in circles, Baptists clap, lamas move their hands through ritual gestures, Hassidim daven, Sufis spin in white gowns, Chinese walk T'ai Chi, priests raise the Host.

Now we add other subroutines. To prepare the aural cortex, we repeat a familiar line of syllables in our mind over and over. It can be a prayer, it can be a mantra, it can be a hope or a dream. Hare Ram, Hail Mary, Kyrie Eleison, Praise God. We repeat it until it comes without any thought at all. To focus the emotions of the already excited limbic system, we direct our mood to openness and vulnerability. We keep our eyes fixed on the altar, the image, the candle, or even the mental image we have memorized, keeping our visual cortex in a similar state of synthetic repetitive overstimulation. To saturate the prefrontal lobes, the future forecasters and time sequencers, we project the same hope, and our faith in that future. All of these we repeat together, over and over and over again. Eventually we will have created such a huge network that if the hormones hit, the higher brain might go up like a munitions dump, dissolving ego into the arms of Eternal Father, Mother, God, Allah, Buddha, Brahma, Abraham, Ahura Mazda or whatever our culture has taught us to call the universal one and only timeless state of grace.

Once again, we are using electrochemistry to lift the roof off its lintels, but it is the only way that we can become oracles ourselves. It can easily leave the unprepared babbling nonsense syllables until normal processing is restored. By synchronizing the right physical and mental practices, we can greet God, join with Jesus, ally with Allah, rally with Ram, dissolve in the Dharma, and come back blessed. Real spiritual masters and saints know how to do this from a standing start but they have been working at it a lot longer than most of us. Any apparent short cuts, either through compulsive religious activity or the powerful mental and physical practices of Asian meditative and tantric traditions, can actually be harmful to the unprepared, leading not only to hurt feelings and headaches but mild mental derangement as well.

Luckily, there are so many forms of gentler activity, both with others and by ourselves, that our personal meditative or devotional practices can easily be integrated into our lives. In time, our keys to the good times become easier to find as we find sincere ways to lose ourselves not out of

our minds, but very deeply into our minds. There we will find the answers we were looking for, and often when we least expect them. It is
interesting to speculate when, and how, the practice of complex inter-
locking repetitious physical and mental activity could have triggered the
first transcendental experience. One possible scenario could have been
the shuffling "dance" around the guard-fire in front of the cave or the
lean-to.

It is very, very late at night. The wind is arid and warm in the dry season, when even the grasses dry up and the small bands of humans must
move continually from place to place seeking water and food. We are
back to the time before history, probably more than a hundred thousand
years ago. This was the real garden of Eden, primeval and unaware,
without priest and without prophet. The brain is now large enough that
our early ancestors were finally living as much by their plans as by their
primitive weapons. Life was harsh, and the dry season was harsher. The
small "family" is asleep, and the hunter is keeping watch. The darkness
surrounds him with sounds and stirrings.

Beyond the faint light of the flickering coals are the jackals and the
hyenas. They are hungrier than the hunter, and he knows it. The woman
is asleep, their infant is ill, and still he must shuffle about the fire. If it
dies, if he falters, the animals will come. He knows that too. By himself,
or with a brother or clan cousin, night after night he shuffles about the
fire, waving his throwing-stick, shouting hoarsely into the darkness
where the eyes lie waiting. Hour after hour it continues; the coals glowing at the center of his exhausted circle, the waving stick, the waves of
memories and hopes, always the same, echoing through the auditory cortex in unspoken supplication.

"Come dawn, come morning light, come before I fall asleep, come to
save me from this night of darkness, this night of fear."

It may not have been spoken aloud, it may not have been in words, but
it was the seed of what would become a chant or a prayer. All night the
endless circling, the same movements, the smokey smell of the fire exciting the olfactory cortex and priming the hippocampus, the same words,
the same thoughts exhausting one layer of cells after another in the auditory cortex, the visual cortex fixed on the glowing fire against the black-
ness of night, blurring, circling. His eyes grow bleary; his droning chant
continues as he beseeches the sun to rise.

How many nights had he shuffled in that circle? It was almost every night as they camped across that dry African savannah. Every night the same ritual would be repeated, the same endless dance, the same exhausted prayer. The combinations would have all been there. Rhythmic movement of a watchful nature, neural exhaustion at the perceptive level, overstimulated limbic system, a consciousness filled with feelings of helplessness and longing. It was probably the same for Moses, lost in a desert sunset in the Sinai or for Saul, about to be Paul, swaying in rhythm back and forth under a hot sun on the back of a donkey carrying him to Damascus. Gautama sat famished at the base of a tree as Sujata approached, Mohammed prayed, isolated in a cave in the desert hills. Saviors and prophets, intense, searching, all looking for their inner light. The truth speaks out of the sky, out of blazing bushes, from angels, and in meditation, and it can be pretty violent the first time. It knocked Paul right off his donkey, converting him on the spot. Moses exited to start the Exodus, Buddha found the Four Noble Truths, Mohammed wrote the Koran, and Mirabai and Sri Chaitanya danced in joy from town to town.

Back in the endless rhythms of a prehistoric night, our ancient ancestor is in an autohypnotic state. His movements are nearly on autopilot, his exhausted consciousness at the sleep threshold, his eyes barely open. Sleep tugs at his mind. He falters, and the throwing stick clatters onto the rocks. He lunges forward, skips a beat, trips and stumbles towards the fire. He jerks back, the flames leap, a jackal howls a dozen feet behind him and it is suddenly just too much. The howl makes it to the aural cortex but the associative networks are starting to unravel in overload. Signals break down as swarms of neurotransmitters clog uptake slots but there's not enough room. It's just too much to handle. In waves, unleashed chaos begins to surge through the overloaded neural channels, collapsing the basic platforms of consciousness like floors in a collapsing building, plunging the hunter into the fail-safe of sheer being. As his cognitive world dissolves in uncontrolled neural saturation, consciousness veers into pure asynchronous reality without any limbic limitations.

He staggers, momentarily stunned, and drops heavily to his knees before the fire. Is this death? The world sways and sparkles; he reaches out towards his sleeping mate and child. His companions, awakened now, see it all. What is he doing at the fire? Inside his bowed head, the whole history of his labors and devotions are avalanching into the present moment and his body swims in hormonal shock. The overstimulated and exhausted cerebral lobes blank out, the cerebellum seizes, the prefrontal lobes wail a chorus to the brain stem, the hippocampus joins in and the limbic system disinhibits. An adrenal rush floods his veins just as reality suddenly unhinges. Anything is real now and anything can be real. The hunter jerks upright like a puppet on a string. The hormonal surge hits the visual cortex. His vision clears, his movements are sure and confident and his limbs glow with inner fire. His prayers are answered; God has just kissed him on the top of his brain and he knows that he is the one and only beloved. More than that, he is strong, and he is chosen! Heart pounding, he strides in slow motion to where he keeps his stone axe, grabs it like a toy, and screaming like a demon dashes into the night, smashing jackals into jackal chops.

The first time was unrecorded but it happened, and when they came to him the next day with the gifts and the fearful respect, there was something new on earth. He had discovered the first internal connection to something beyond ourselves, something that made us much more than ourselves. We, in turn, had discovered the first holy man. There would be many more.

Varieties of Grace: Taking the Time

If our paleolithic hero learns to go through all those various preliminaries exactly the same way again, or if he's done it enough times, or if he adds any plant intoxicants for a little booster, he may become the first shaman. Over many millennia, the fire and the steps became stylized, weapons and implements became sacred objects, and heartfelt utterances were formalized into chants and prayers. The holy wisdom took words, and was made poetic, but it was always the same eloquently expressed human common sense articulated by those gifted with a universal perspective beyond the virtual reality of personal time and space. The ability to combine those activities which could together create an interlinked symphony of hormonal and electrochemical overload became a secret understanding, unspoken, and still acknowledged with great difficulty by those who have been touched by it. It has not been, nor will it ever be adequately described because it is a temporary brush with the mind we knew before we knew speech. In fact, the experience often leaves us speechless.

The many paths to a renewed vision eventually became bound into religious and mystic traditions wherever humans live, embodied in innumerable cultural variants wherever there is a priesthood and a tradition. We are actually familiar with many forms of mental and emotional self-cleansing, experiences which may provide some with insight, others with wisdom, and all a richer experience of life. All religions, cults, and even newer holistic philosophies have these practices available within them. For any Christian who seeks a stronger faith there are polite prayer groups or passionate Pentecostal preachers to raise the spirit. The Orthodox Jew sways at shul, his kids kibitz with the Kabbala. Muslims can swirl with dervishes, follow Sufi saints, or engage in Shiite S&M, smiting themselves with stones in a Farsi frenzy. Hindus and Buddhists have a particularly rich collection of meditative and tantric practices which serve to unlayer and massage the mind in precise degrees. Depending on how far we wish to take our involvement, we can self generate everything from the warm glow of compassionate fellowship with co-religionists to the nearly uncontrollable full adrenalin surges found in ecstatic singing, talking, and dancing.

We can, over time, learn to let go the ego just enough to work a little better with our friends, or go all the way and dissolve our personality into the mind of the universe. The chant can be "Hail Mary," "Allahu Akbar," "Om Mane Padme Hum," "Amida Butsu," "Nam-yo-ho, Renge-kyo" or "Hare Krishna." They all work equally well, so say "Hallelujah," "Amen," and "Thank you, Jesus." If we wanted, any of us could devise personal movements, mantras, prayers, and rituals. With enough practice they would probably do just as well. On the other hand, it's easier on the personal emotional traditions of our limbic system to use a method historically familiar and culturally natural to us. If we want to believe in one religion or another, or even just make use of helpful devotional or meditative practices, it is easier to find inspiration within our own culture. Anyone can get to Krishna with enough devotion, but getting to Jesus may be easier for a lapsed Christian who was once the child who loved Bible stories.

Once we are familiar with some of the neurological staging behind our transcendental forms of pleasure seeking, it should come as no surprise that none of this can be accomplished without patient and sincere practice. We can't rush biochemistry, nor can we ever predict when we will harness enough of our mental energy to dissolve chronology and share the incomparable experience. As Diana Ross put it so simply, "You can't hurry love, no, you just have to wait." This is probably why both St. Paul and John Calvin stressed that one cannot obtain heaven with deeds and why Buddhist tradition insists on lifetimes of mindful practice. To even start our journey to our fulfillment we must be focused on our daily life and the pleasures we find on a moment to moment basis. Our attention must be in the present tense, not wandering about in our past or our expectations of some future fulfillment.

As it happens, humans are eminently trainable into this sort of self-improvement. Real blessings and a growing enlightenment can arrive in less than a few years, often when we least expect it. If we prepare ourselves and practice faithfully, fulfillment will come looking for anyone who is really ready to accept it, and it inevitably arrives in the present tense. When traditional prayers or practices are done with any consistency, there will always come a time when the practitioner will begin to notice that the world is, for some reason, looking better and more inviting. If we feed the mind a more balanced diet, each well experienced day filed away creates expectations of a similar future. We can't change our chaotically woven system of human consciousness, but we can load up the loom with good times and start to watch the patterns change. We can even darn up the holes in the networks we don't like, and fine tune our virtual reality to the tunes we like to hear.

The whole purpose, of course, is to reach the point in our life where from a Western religious perspective the kingdom of God is at hand or from an Eastern perspective that we are in the Dharma or the Tao, on our true and natural path. From a systems approach, we would say that we acquired debugging utilities that can override the cycling glitch in the original software, letting us reset our goals and restart our life. Whatever the path we choose, our purpose will be revealed in the manner that life itself becomes more inviting than any talk show, soap opera, historical romance, or future cash flow. In reviving and maintaining a full and active involvement in the world around us, we are freed from the gridlock of virtual ego and returned, reborn, to an exciting, moving world with a peaceful, personal center.

Unfortunately, a lack of rational perspectives on religious belief and practice has had the backward effect of fostering, and even promoting, a trend towards mindless emotional and devotional fundamentalism in nearly every major world religion. Denied a universal, and thereby a generic, guidebook and route to the mystical experience and the personal security it can bring, stressed-out seekers in every nation are being easily manipulated into trading personal will, common sense, and even basic decency for the reassurances of dogmatic certainty.

Our growing need for some sense of ultimate authority in this confusing time of global religious mixing and matching seems to have re-established all the self-appointed guardians of the words of God, be it Gospel, Torah, Koran, Sutra, or Say-So. Hoards are herded into the presence of self-promoting swamis of the popular priesthood, all promising bliss and belief for simply surrendering all to this guide, that guru, Gee-Whiz or Jay-zuz. Promising that we can leave all the questions in the world to some higher power, media mega-mullahs use mobs of orchestrated followers singing, praying, swaying, and chanting to pump up the stimulation levels and hormonally hype unsuspecting souls through the portals of glory. Sinners are slain in the spirit for Jesus Christ, while Hindu devotees experience shaktipat with a mantra and a touch. Preachers promising easy certainties swarm in times such as these, taking advantage of national and worldwide stress and frustration to promote their simplistic solutions and the synthetic reassurance of intense and exclusive ritual.

As might be expected, few of these shortcuts to Shangri-la have lasting effects. Without the steady and consistent repetition of positive, thoughtful action required to create the natural neural networks and mental associations, these spiritual super salesmen have to continually hammer their followers into adrenal excess with everything from "love bombing" to fire walks. If the message has to be channelled it's time to change the channels; when they start waving the holy books, it's time to wave goodbye. Real priests, pandits, mullahs, and ministers generally avoid this forced rock 'n roll of the nervous system. There is a good reason that Jesus directed his followers to pray in the privacy of their rooms and why the Buddha directed his students to find calm and quiet places for meditation. The practices which reach the deepest are truly self-tailored, they are not group events; they are personal and they are precious.

Those drawn to complex ceremony and ritual rarely have time to reach out to others who do not dance in the same circle or chant the same prayers to the same God or guide. The sincere and simple paths to empowerment are there to lift us out of both past and future and rededicate us again to the present; the only place shared by us all. In truly finding ourselves again we are not confined to co-practitioners, we are liberated to go and involve ourselves even more fully in the world around us. The big secret, if there ever were one, is that each of us has, within us, the ability to do it all by ourselves.

Seeking true self-fulfillment for a human, then, is nearly the opposite of the rat with its pleasure button. While animals drive themselves quickly to exhaustion, only a small percentage of humans are that compulsive. In fact, most of us do learn to enjoy the conscious generation of joy and happiness as a regular experience, just to make life itself more vibrant. We can get excited about our art, our craft, our dance, our friends, our family, our skills, and even our mystical mental spirituality. We can all learn to live inside, and outside, our limits, learning about ourselves daily in a full involvement with the life we are actually living.

Living with a fully evolved human consciousness, we have some unique problems. We slip easily into so many forms of mental mind block, cycling, and repetition, not to mention getting caught in the grid-lock of chronological time. On the other hand, it seems that we have developed some awesome mental upgrading routines and even specific applications to enhance and improve our own consciousness. Putting them into practice, we see why the great religious leaders had so little to say about ritual. Jesus never mentions speaking in tongues, nor did Mohammed do Sufi dances. The Buddha walked with his monks, teaching from town to town; he did not sit chanting in a cave. Our guides were not telling us to give up on life, but to give out to life and enjoy the greater community of the entire human family.

We can always find ourselves by being a little more selfless; we have a guarantee of pleasure with every kindness we show another. This is why they all speak not of power and wealth, but of simple consideration, forgiveness, generosity, and above all, love and kindness. These are the sorts of pleasures that only humans know anything about, and in practicing them, they bring us always closer to the best of our own humanity. If God is in our image, that is when God smiles; we are manifesting divinity and anyone who has known a moment of that shared happiness knows just how it feels.

As natural pleasure seekers, then, we have such a lot of ways that we can travel. There is everything from full blown fantasy to real self discovery and all the stages in between. We can be angry at life's obstacles and get our excitement stressfully or we can be enthusiastic about life's challenges and get it sweet. We can all find our ways to make life as stimulating as we want it to be, and we usually use the ways we've gotten used to. But the careful and graduated steps to inner tranquility and personal fulfillment are also there, and available to all with the will to improve and the patience to keep at it. Day by day, step by step, and moment by moment we can reweave the tapestry of our own virtual perception with mindful attention to our craft, our art, our hopes, our practice, and our prayers. We can re-pattern our mind for easy gladness, and make personal happiness into a habit.

Our tools may be molecules, and heavenly experiences are still dependent on hormonal states, but we can get an entirely new outlook if we give it a try. This is one world that gives us more chances for a good time than we ever thought possible. It is, after all, Eden, Shambhala, Fat City, and the Kingdom of God; and we are right smack in the middle of it. In going beyond our personal, cultural, and even conscious limitations, we have the chance to finally awaken to a better world, the one that we all share, the one where we all can care. We just have to take the simple steps to reach that new perspective, and the vision will change us forever. In Sanskrit they say, *Gate, Gate, Paragate, Parasamgate, Bhodi, Svaha.* Go, go, go beyond, go completely beyond, awaken, and rejoice. We're here; that's all, that's it, know it, be it, enjoy it, and be eternally grateful. Our world is heading for better times, and each of us is a living part of it. We can have faith in this, and do our part, with kindness and the gentle heart.

10

Soul Survivors

What Really Happens When We Die

Life is a lifetime falling into death. From birth we trace an arc, tossed up into the living for a time; but even as we are loosed into life our destiny is determined. Life, it seems, has a catch to it. There is an end of it. Eventually we must touch down, and we hope the catch is gentle.

As children, we think nothing of it, too taken with our vital present to imagine a finite future, but as we grow older we begin to notice mortality and before long we know that we are not everlasting. Long before we fully comprehend the certainty of our temporary existence we pray that God will take us into heaven when we die. Wherever that is. Whenever that is. As adults, we interpret it all to the young, trying to explain the reasons behind the experience of life. But when it comes to something as common as dying, we are all still like children. We know where Santa Claus gets the toys, and where the Easter bunny gets the baskets, but most of us are still hopefully expecting that if we die before we wake, we trust the Lord our soul to take. Even the most rational among us usually agree that when it comes to that inevitable, ultimate, and final transition, God only knows what happens then.

For many more, avoidance is the best refuge against a disturbing realization. As the world population grows, we notice more and more people dying all the time. It's clearly more than a trend. So, we keep our minds fixed on the here and now rather than the where and when. We live all our lives, and then . . .

And then . . . will the heavenly odds-maker collect the bets and the first person to the other side please tell us what happened? Am I Brahman, a spirit, or an angel? Did Jesus love me, or did it turn out to be Nirvana and I'm being returned as a turtle for some Buddhist sin? Are these the Elysian Fields, the Happy Hunting Grounds or, wrong turn, doggy heaven for Rover? The more we think about it, the more we realize how undefined this most inevitable of destinations remains. We know more about the moon than the experience of death, and very few have gone to the moon. Those that went, however, returned, and that is the difference. The moon is a temporary destination; death is always forever.

Where, or how, we spend that forever remains for too many a bothersome unanswered question. This is an innocence nearly all of us keep throughout life, with much guesswork and very few authorities. We cannot speak with authority ourselves, and those with real expertise have nothing to say at all. Dead men tell no tales. And so, preferring something to nothing, many accept the various descriptions of everlasting life, or lives, as described by traditional religious or spiritual beliefs. Those who have found a path they can trust know the peace of the mighty and the comfort of the meek. As we grew older, we began to understand that we all want it. If truth were told, nearly all the non-believers would love to have a reason to believe.

Uncommon Destinations: Traditional Views of Heaven and Hell

Comparing the afterlives of the world's great religions, there seem to be many similarities. At first, singing in angelic Christian choirs doesn't seem quite like getting off Buddha's wheel of life, but there is always the ultimate peace. It is always a journey or a return to a higher and better place where the woes of life on earth are left behind as we take up a bright new existence in a new world, an eternal world without end.

Living in the cross-cultural currents of our new global society, it is sometimes hard to remember that less than a hundred years ago, wherever we were, we were either a believer or an infidel. Today, although fundamentalist sects of major world religions still bar non-believers from heaven, most thinking people would agree that Gandhi was working on the same wavelength as Mother Theresa and allow for cultural variations. This was unthinkable a century ago when major world religions were more geographically centered. But what about death and beyond?

Most religions seem to share a general consensus about a number of stages. At some point of time between when we stop breathing and start coming apart, the non-physical part of us (soul, mind, spirit, atman, etc.) takes a journey to another place. The mortal body, which was created at the same time as the eternal part, or which houses it during this life, proceeds to compost. However, the soul, spirit, etc., continues to exist in a mindful, if disincorporated, fashion as it starts its journey onward.

There may be an initial purging, depending on what we did during our life on earth. The Purgatory of Roman Catholicism has its similarities to the Tibetan's frightening Bar-do world between lives. Swedenborgian theology prescribes a time in a spirit world to make us fit to meet God. It's important to note that it seems we cannot stay in these places indefinitely. Whether time in a purgatory or a few extra lives to clean up the karma, sooner or later we progress. This is all for ordinary people of course; true saints go directly to the good place and real evildoers go straight to the bad place.

Then comes judgment. Our deeds are totalled, our purgations accounted for, and we are assigned to a far longer stay somewhere else. If we are now acceptable, we go to heaven, or Brahman, or Nirvana, or the Pure Lands, and stay there forever; if not, back to purging, more lives, or worse. Most eventually get to a nice eternity, which comes in nearly every variety depending on the time, culture, and nature of the writer. A Catholic who made it to the most common heaven of the Buddhists, rebirth in the Pure Lands, would probably assume that Franciscans had charge of eternity in this merciful agrarian paradise. The displeasure of the Viking waking up in Jewish *Sheol*, a very sober place, when he expected the eternal fraternity party of Valhalla is not recorded in language we can repeat here. Mormons enshrine marriage on earth, so in Mormon heaven you keep your mate, but a blessed Muslim male may meet dozens of beautiful women in Islamic bliss. Serious Christians become joyous celibates while celibate old Himalayan monks could find themselves manifested as minor tantric deities in eternal sexual union with the appropriate consort, complete with four arms, a rosary, and a yak-tail fly whisk.

Hell, likewise, seems to vary to the extent one takes a literal interpretation of the Holy Word. In the hot lands of the Middle East, birthplace of Judaism, Christianity, and Islam, cool is heavenly so hell was hotter than blazes. Ironically, the word "hell" is taken from the Norse underworld, an abode locked in everlasting snow and ice. They would have loved some heat in original Hell, where frost giants stalked and cold was the killer. Buddhist scriptures describe both hot and cold hells, further subdivided by Tibetans into picturesque categories and names such as "a-choo," a sort of endless cold in the nose. This may be why orthodox Taoists borrow Buddhist heavens, but choose Taoist hells. Jains have the most hells, exactly 8.4 million, but the Muslim *Jahannam* seems to be exactly the same place as the Hebrew hell *Gehenna*, a truly hellish prospect for any evil Arab.

The reason that hell is still not the final judgment is that all hells seem to have a back door to them. An abjectly bad Buddhist will simply be recycled in rebirth after rebirth until his karma is all gone, no matter how long it takes. Christians have until the very last moment to make peace with God. Even if an evil unfortunate ends up in the place with the pitchforks, the message of Christ promises forgiveness whenever true repentance appears. Since the Second Vatican Council, this last chance option has been official for Catholics, but it's been Hindu faith forever. Even the most sinful swami could return only so many times as a Calcutta street beggar without getting back on the straight track to Shiva after a while. It's just the trip which is longer and rougher for some than it is for others.

Since most, if not all of unpleasant detours are apparently incurred or avoided by the manner in which we live this present life, religious teachers provide insights and methods useful not only to us now, but able to transport us to a good eternity without too many intermediate stops in those unpleasant places. In fact, one of the ways by which we can distinguish one religion from another is by their afterlife . The great saints speak similar wisdom in differing tongues, but the Pope and the Dalai Lama have distinctly different retirement homes when their good works are done. The reward of Christianity is instant heaven, while the enlightened Boddhisattva is recycled for future lives spent helping others. This is eternal, either way.

Once the journey is over, we spend the rest of forever in the nicest place imaginable. Theologians write of everlasting oneness; those with more vivid imaginations have for centuries expounded on the unspeakable, ineffable, glorious, indescribable and so on, last stop. It's always our eternal home, always just what we wanted. Like happy, heaven seems the same to all peoples and still very personal to each of us.

Death, not life, seems to be the force that unites us all and yet still, it separates us. We all die and we all journey on, but regional religions still tend to determine our personal beliefs and faithful expectations. Those without faith suspect such expectations are pure romance, but most still hope to find the place their cultural religious faith has always promised.

Afterlife explanations may come in many languages, but they all seem to describe the same experiences. Different guides report scenery appropriate to their custom and culture, but all cover the same territory and come to the same place when earthly time stops and eternity begins. The promise is always fulfilled; by God, by Allah, or by the Dharma. The steps are so regular and consecutive as to suggest a common heavenly blueprint. Might there be a basic, underlying, universal pathway to the beyond? Again the possibility arises. Could this be neurological phenomena? So far, the neural process itself seems to answer most of the questions which appear to be human rather than cultural. Death must be the grand-daddy of them all, the biggest question in the mind of mankind. Is it answerable?

The main problem is that although we are all promised appropriate afterlives, no scripture explains just how we shift over to this timeless universe that seems to appear only when we are dead and gone. None come with a shop manual to describe how we can accomplish this leap to immortality given the only tools at hand: our old, sick, dying mortal selves. These days, most of us don't like to believe in magic. If it's really possible, it's time we came up with an explanation that makes sense.

Now that modern medical technology seems to be able to keep any of us, or for that matter any part of us, alive with various devices nearly indefinitely, there is a renewed interest in just what happens afterward. No one in recent history has died and returned to life and nobody yet has been known to survive brain death. We do have, however, volumes of reports from those who got close enough to stick a toe across and beat it back before too late. By reviewing available information, we begin to get a picture of death that may help guide us towards the explanation we seek.

The physical requirements for normal consciousness are simple and absolutely quantifiable. Our brain requires 3.3 ml. of oxygen for every 100 grams of mass per minute and a blood glucose level of 80-120 mg. per 100 ml. It must eliminate waste toxins, and it requires the right blood pressure. Every aspect of brain function has precise requirements and limitations. It can't survive ten minutes without oxygen. Anything that interrupts blood flow stops everything. The result, in every case aside from severe brain mutilation, is brain coma.

Almost all of us will lapse into brain coma before we die, but each year a few make it back without permanent brain damage and describe the experiences they had. A number of survivors of these near-death experiences were cataloged for similarities by Dr. Kenneth Ring, one of the first physicians to conduct serious research into these phenomena. Placed in the order they were perceived, these reports suggest a series of common experiences. Subjects reported "peace and contentment" (60%), "detachment from the physical body" (37%), "entering the darkness" (23%), "seeing the light" (16%) and "entering the light" (11%).

Since most patients who suffer the sort of trauma experienced by these individuals do not recover, survival ratios would naturally favor those who experienced only the first stages of brain coma. The low percent reporting "entering the light" is probably because most of those who get that far don't revive. Along with these near-death revival stories, there are the last words of those who died describing their final visions, often leaving poignant images of a place beyond. Interestingly, these visions are almost uniformly pleasant and often include parents or other relatives and friends who had died before. Finally, there are the descriptions from skilled Indian swamis and Tibetan masters of meditative technique. These adepts seem to have held onto their minds fiercely through their last few moments, reporting everything they were experiencing until even they fell silent.

There are many common themes: a miraculous transformation, leaving the physical body, heavenly beings, a bright light, and a final peaceful merging. Only the details seem to be cultural. Nirvana never arrives for a devout Dominican nun. Holy Hindus drop their bodies and achieve samadhi but they never meet Mother Mary. It is our own life that we reexperience, our own relatives who greet us along the way. Left unanswered is how we can greet our grandparents if they are off with their own grandparents: the paradox of the infant grannies. Holy books seem strangely incomplete; the inevitable crowds of Chinese in paradise are simply not mentioned in any Christian Biblical text. Even heavenly angels meet cultural expectations; winged for Christian, non-winged for Hindus. Heaven is always a curious combination of human universals and cultural specifics.

As all human cultures have religions, it seems very likely that those images common to all religions just might be common to human consciousness. As these same images appear both in the sayings of revered prophets and from first-hand reports of near-death, or "clinical" death and revival, it does suggest that there might be a neurological explanation for it. Saviors and prophets have always been able to tell us where we went after death; it seems that science may finally be ready to provide a reasonable explanation of how we actually get there.

Welcome Home: Return To Eternity

So what happens at death? By now the nature of the experience of death may be apparent to some already. If we once spent forever winding up the mental clock that ticks us through time and space, that endless time between conception and age three, it will take just as long to wind it down. The human brain at the point of death has billions of fully functional neurons. Each one is different, each is alive. As death arrives, they cannot all suddenly jump up and die at the same moment. That would be impossible. They die off over some period of time, and their more sensitive functions go first. From the most sensitive dendrites on the most exposed cortical cells to the most embedded neurons in the brain stem, the brain dies by degrees. Our chips will unplug one at a time as our mental network simplifies around us. As our brain dies step by step, our mind will gently unwind.

Since it is the activity of the human brain which permits and limits our awareness of anything else, how will our awareness change as the brain changes during the time of death? Unless the brain is physically destroyed, the stages of brain death cannot vary much from one person to another. We have known many forms of consciousness since our unborn days when our brain was a fraction of its current mass or complexity. We're bound to lose our more recent mental capabilities long before we reach any final end. From a strictly medical point of view, the brain will begin to sustain irreparable damage at normal temperature after ten minutes without oxygen. This does not suggest, however, that during normal human brain death the major biological supports of consciousness could instantly collapse all at once. In other words, even if we wanted to we couldn't just pull the plug on consciousness. It must simplify in a somewhat predictable progression.

As we die, we fall into irreversible brain coma. Brain coma, however, is not by any means the end. It is the end of this worldly consciousness, but also a return to an earlier form of consciousness and an earlier universe. In sleep, normal waking consciousness does not operate as the brain goes through its necessary rest and recreation, exercising some functions while letting others doze. We have all had dreams that seemed to last ages, only to waken and discover we had been asleep only a few minutes. When the time sequencing system in the prefrontal lobes goes off-line, dreams can pack months into moments. So what triggers these time-distorted worlds we call dreams?

Harvard researcher Alan Hobson believes that dreams are neither Freudian films nor mystical guides, but merely artifacts created by stimulating the higher brain centers with irregular bursts of neural static from the brain stem during sleep. Emotional states aroused in this manner take visual form, but time and abstraction are off-line. This is a small example of how an "unconscious" mind can fully experience a consciousness unattached to worldly perception. The very important difference is that as we only dream with images synthesized from memory, people and events in our dreams can only be woven from our own personal experience up to that point.

No matter what our cause of death, then, consciousness must go unconscious before death comes. This means that we can still be aware, unconscious but in a dream-like state, even as the brain dies; cells winking out at random, axons sending their final messages, dendrites reacting, failing, and finally falling silent. The experience of the simplification of our brain would be perceived as the gradual simplification of our mind over a period of time which will seem endless. As the neural nets unravel, we will gradually return to the endless eternity of the undifferentiated mind that we knew since we were created and long before we were born.

The progressive stages of brain death specifically responsible for the basic near-death sequences as reported by Ring's subjects have been known for some time. They were collected and put into general order recently by Canadian neurosurgeon Leslie Ivan. The brain starts to die as the delicate balance of its blood biochemistry begins to change. Usually, something interferes with oxygenation and as the oxygen levels drop, neural firing rate begins to decrease. This is what tranquilizers do, and it creates the pleasant, dreamy "peace and contentment" felt by so many near death.

The buildup of carbon dioxide and other toxins in the blood now start to create distortions in cortical firing patterns while deep in the limbic system, specific endorphin receptors begin to react to the falling oxygen levels. Generalized physical sensations, disassociation from the body, and even euphoria begin to occur. At about the same time, the visual cortex begins to fail along with the chronological sequencing structures in the prefrontal lobes. Our sense of time and space begin to bend us gently back towards our beginnings.

Our memories and emotions are loosed from time control; images from the past begin to flood a consciousness which is no longer either exact or discriminating. It is the same endorphin mix we remember from our birth as we begin to retrace our ancient path. Soon, either blood loss or changes in blood chemistry have progressed so far that cortical brain cells are beginning to die at random. The visual cortex is a sensitive and sophisticated structure relatively near the surface of the brain and therefore especially vulnerable. Visual memory patterns lose definition and fade. Nerve cells in the visual cortex begin to disconnect and die. The inhibitory rule structures of our virtual reality crash as uncontrolled neural hyperactivity creates vivid images and timeless dream sequences from random energy. As the visual cortex continues to simplify, the color scale begins to alter and dissolve back to the earliest color we knew, our primeval red, not the fires of hell but the endless sunset that finally fades to the familiar darkness we knew from the very beginning, before our own dawning, before we were born.

The darkness begins to surround us. Beyond the red sunset, there remains the dull glow. Consciousness is quickly losing the last edge of specific definition as the continued destruction of the neural networks increases. The last fits and starts illuminate the great ocean of oneness with pinpoints of blazing energy, the stars, the lights we see, as we head into our new old universe. We are among the stars now and we begin to move towards the distant light. That light is the last signal of all, when all signals from this universe have faded into the starry night. Like our last call from this earth, our old reality filter, the dying reticular activating system, surges, yanking consciousness tight for a final moment. We sign our names in this universe for the last time, and return to our final home. When we finally get there, we will enter the light; and become the light. We know where we are going on our last journey because we came this way before. Now we return.

Each of us will, in time, one at a time, join in this final shared experi-ence. We must travel together with the mind that made us as the weave is gently unwoven . As our brain, the great analyzer and discriminator, moves moment by moment to the final and ultimate simplicity of one last cell, we are moving with it. At no time can we be aware that it is we that are simplifying; a simpler mind cannot know concepts which require a brain that is no longer capable of discriminating thought. We are now moving backwards into ancient memories we could never remember on earth, woven in a simpler time. We are returning to the other universe we know, the universe we always knew, our old eternal home. Where do we make our transcendant ascension? Probably between our disassocia-tion from the body and the light, which is as far as has been reported. The most detailed reports so far have come from some highly trained Tibetan lamas whose last words were characterized by very specific de-scriptions of the stages in the dissolution of their worldly consciousness. The sequence, as described by the Venerable Lati Rinpoche and Professor Jeffrey Hopkins of the University of Virginia, even includes changes in the color of the sky as one begins the final journey onward into the Bar-do, the gone-beyond.

The dream sky at the beginning of death is initially bright white. White is the mixture of all colors at equal intensity, a good description of what the background would look like in early brain coma if the visual cortex had disinhibited. We will see the color of all colors when the vi-sual controls start to falter. As time begins to go timeless, we lose visual definition and the sky slowly fades to red, the lowest color in the human visual color spectrum and the earliest color we knew. According to the Tibetans, we then see "points of light, like sparks." Finally there comes darkness and the "setting face to face with the clear light of death." We are returning to the universe we knew before birth, back to when we *were* the only known universe, the only one we'd ever known. There is still a lot of brain left; but we are now as timeless and as sightless as our sev-enth month in the womb. We are the one and only again, this time for-ever.

Scientists prefer independent verification for theories that the mind may still be perceiving cogently even as the brain is simplifying during death. Without a single scanner and the most rudimentary knowledge of

brain science, the lamas had been describing in sequence the gradual
death of the brain while the event was actually in progress. They never
went beyond the "clear light of death" in their lucid descriptions; by that
time they had stopped talking and "gone beyond" to the most profound
and universal state of mind we will ever encounter in our lives. It is a return to our beginning; the circle is now one, eternity to eternity, and all in
one lifetime.

This does seem to be our path; but what is the actual personal experience? It is probably a blessed event, as gently reassuring as our birth was
once so bewildering, when was it, a few moments ago? With timelessness fast approaching, our lifetime will seem to have been but a short so-
journ, almost a dream, in some strange other world. As discrimination
falters, we will begin again to remember forever, see again the sights we
saw when we had just arrived from where we are now returning. Tall
beings, past lives, the rounds of judgement and rounds of forgiveness; the
long forgotten past returns as time itself begins to stretch out moment by
moment.

Years appear now between the minutes of earthly time, centuries between seconds, eons between the tenths of seconds. Finally, as was
promised by our God, or our faith, we are returned to oneness forever, for
had there ever been anything else? By then, we cannot perceive anything
else. By that time we are eternal, as the heart, the mind, the soul, and the
universe all merge in the journey back to one, the journey which will
never end. Eternity arrives early. It comes with our final consciousness
and it comes for us just a few minutes before physical brain death. We
will never be able to perceive death itself; we will run out of time and
self long before it gets to us. The final catch is gentle indeed; we have
nothing at all to worry about. We all go home in the end to the timelessness of another universe which can remember nothing, and is forever.

Although this description of the simplification of consciousness agrees
with information we have from the scientific community, it must remain
speculative. Final confirmation remains impossible because of the nature
of life; there is a threshold below which a dying cell is dead and unreviv-
able. Anything which would take consciousness to a completely uncom-
parative, timeless state would probably kill off so many brain cells in the
process that we might as well stay there. If revived, we would suffer
from hopeless brain damage, remaining trapped in a body completely in-
appropriate to our mental state. When faced with the question of remov-

ing life support from the brain dead, Pope Pius XII suggested that, in irreversible coma, the soul might have already left the body. He was right, and in even suggesting it he was demonstrating how easily religion can incorporate neurological perspective as a backup for wisdom that was always available. Still, the final proof will always be missing. Our best witnesses leave us before it's over.

Among the living, then, we can have no trustworthy reporters. Brains and minds in the midst of organization towards complexity are in the heads of people too young to speak and as yet unable to reason. Likewise, dying people end with their dying words; we never hear about their final destination. The Book of the Dead must still be read on faith, but it seems that it is not an unreasonable hope to expect eternity. In fact, there seems no way to avoid it. Due to the phenomena of time distortion, which must occur as we lose chronological controls, there is no way to know how long it takes to regress consciousness back to eternity. Brain cells are capable of firing hundreds of times in a second; we could slow down to a graceful end in the blink of an eye. By the time we reach our own ancient universe, time effectively will have stopped for each of us.

In 1992, my mother had a stroke. Her CAT scans showed three fifths of her right hemisphere was gone. Still, her prefrontal cortex and her visual cortex were spared. Paralyzed on the left side and frequently confused due to the massive trauma, she was still able to correctly identify the brain artery which had been blocked and remained conversant, emotionally subtle, and aware. Within a month, an undetected infection destroyed her functioning left hemisphere over a period of about a week. There could be no gentler death than having the brain die in such a slow, gradual fashion. She had already read this book, and was comforted as many intellectually gifted people are, but in the end she faded to "Jesus Loves Me This I Know" heaven, fulfilled in the faith she had been born into.

Death is usually gentle, but even many violent deaths could not prevent consciousness from going out the slow way. There would be a swifter transfer to unconscious, but then our comfortable and steady return to eternity would begin. Victims of shootings, stabbings, car accidents, or massive loss of blood would always slide into unconsciousness first and then into their final journey without further pain or problems. Common diseases such as cancer, heart attacks, or failures of major organ systems would seem nearly guaranteed to launch us smoothly towards paradise.

Should a boulder drop on our head, however, there might be no death dream experience at all. We would be eternally in the moment before it happened because in a fraction of second all perception would suddenly disappear. Neural impulses travel at about 80 miles per hour; anything that smashes into us going faster than that would slam us into forever faster than we could realize what happened. We would remain forever in the moment before we never saw it coming. We wouldn't miss heaven; in fact we wouldn't miss anything at all. As long as we didn't see it coming.

This brings us to one variety of death that should at all cost be avoided: the violent destruction of the brain while in a disrupted mental state such as panic, pain, misery, or terror. In such an instance, regression could not occur and eternity would be the last consciousness available. Facing the gun that blows your head away or frozen with terror in an injured aircraft that has not gone instantly to pieces could be the worst death of all. For those unable to calm their own minds before such a death, either by religious faith or powerful meditative ability, eternity is dismal. Every religion in the world has its ghosts. They are always, without exception, described as the disconnected souls of those who died a violent death. There was no last option out. For those who ask "What about Hitler?" they now have their answer; most of his victims went to heaven, but by shooting himself in the head, he probably made it impossible for himself. There can be no regression in a brain blown to pieces.

Karma and Compassion: Why it's Good to Be Good

There is a natural justice in the way it seems to work out. If our regression into timelessness is within our own mind, it is within a closed system. Any road to heaven must be paved with our own good intentions, or at least the memories of a life spent that way. At the start of death, we take leave of the open system, the world around us, and enter the closed system that exists only within us. Now our only reality is our virtual reality and we must reside in the world of images we made ourselves. Any recognizable heavenly or hellish scenarios will be mental constructions arising from our dying networks, just as we made our living dream images from mixed-up memories when the forebrain took a nap and time was "off." This time we will join with the dream. We shall not wake again to the world of troubles or pain; we are already long gone beyond that place.

From the neurotheological perspective, this one aspect of brain death provides the impetus for an ethical life more convincingly than any religion currently practiced. It provides a rationale for living a good and decent life that makes better sense than any promise of rebirth, heavenly or otherwise. It has been already demonstrated that we cannot have reality in our minds, just our own virtual reality, our personal neural perception. At birth, and for the first three years, the plasticity of the growing brain prevents the constant repetition that characterizes the mature thinking brain. It is only as we begin to create and extend those larger networks that they become extensive enough to survive the early disorganization of brain function in death.

Infants who die in the womb, soon after birth from birth defects, or even during infancy would naturally have a very easy return since there would be so little repeated experiential detail to disturb a smooth regression to our original mind. However, for most of us, by the time we die we have a lifetime of memories to draw on.

One thing is clear. The path we take during death may be outside the bounds of normal time and space, but it starts inside our heads only after our normal senses have shut down. The outside world ceases to exist, so we can only live among images from our own past personal experience. We are stopped at the point of death and sent packing to eternity with whatever we have put in our heads up to that time. This can be nice for those with minds filled with memories rich with kindness and simple pleasures. However, if we spend a lot of time worrying or stressed, there could be roomfuls of blues that we might endure on our way to wherever after. In the first part of our death experience, everything will be happening at once and forever, but all the imagery must ultimately be derived from our own past.

From this perspective, as far as insuring a pleasant "afterlife" is concerned, what actually happened at any point in our lives will never be as important as what our state of mind was. If we spend a lot of time being hopeful, helpful, kind, generous, supportive and reliable, we should have very nice "endless lifetimes" on the way to the final place. Since we pack our own bags for this trip, we should pack them with care. If we spend a lot of time angry, depressed, selfish, irritable, or withholding, these may be the only backdrops available when the mind takes us timeless. It will seem to be so much longer than our entire life on earth we would probably do well to consider it every day.

This sort of death scenario does substantiate the words of our saints and saviors when it comes to how to live life with respect to the afterlife. If we live a life in emulation of Jesus, by the law of the Prophet, or by the light of the Torah, we should have very little to worry about later; if we make life hard for ourselves and others, we'll take the long and hard way home. It's simply inevitable, any way we look at it.

This is also a very good take on karma. The concept of karma in Asian philosophy speaks directly to the accumulation of neural nets that bias reality and delay enlightenment. Karma happens only with intention, a conscious attention. Intention to do good produces "good karma" and intending to harm creates "bad karma." If we step on a bug that we hadn't noticed there would be no karma, but if we set about looking for a bug and step on it we'd create lots of bad karma. It was where our mind was at the time that makes all the difference. Any real intention requires focussing the mind, creating the sort of deeper memory we might encounter in death. The problem is that if the nets are unravelling, the memory might merge backwards with the memory of another event and we could find ourselves being stepped on by a huge bug in an extended time-frame. Once neural destruction starts, entropy takes over and God only knows what images will emerge as we go through those first stages of forever.

This would agree with Buddhist philosophy stating that we cannot reach Nirvana until all our karma is exhausted. Whether one is going to spend endless lifetimes in wonderful places we created by a good and virtuous life or in various hells and scare shows derived from unpleasant memories, we cannot reach any of the final places until the brain has so simplified that our neural nets can't hold any images any more. In fact, eternity with specifics must be just the first part of the experience. This unusual time and space of "forever first and more later" is made possible because we are not using sequential time any more, Bhairab's special secret in Benares as well as the source of Jesus' life everlasting. We can do eternity in a moment if we turn off time, but we still must reach that final union along the path we made in this one and only life we live on earth. The final judgments here will be only what we know and just rewards are provided to those who have every reason to expect them.

The opposite would also be true, however. There are many forms of suicide which are very gentle, but that is not why religions generally argue against it. The moods which lead to suicide, with the exception of the terminally ill, usually build up over a period of time, deep feelings of helplessness and pain which would not be fun to relive for eternity. This is probably why all orthodox religions have rules against suicide: depression and anger may pass, but our trip to forever never ends. It could be hellish if we don't work it out before we leave. Our human lifetime is the one chance we have to make sure any future lifetimes will be the nice everlasting, even if it all takes place during death.

The Universal Journey: Light unto Light

Luckily, when we really take a good look at our lives most of us are not dissatisfied with them. The great majority of us, therefore, can probably look forward to experiencing this blessed miracle, losing both our perception of earthly time and the discrimination of comparative thought, in one smooth curve down to our last living moment. The beauty of this elegant process, described medically as normal brain death, is that we will find ourselves lost in timelessness before we get half way to the end, and it will take forever to get us even that far. This very personal regression to the infinite is reminiscent of equally unworldly phenomena at quite the opposite end of the size scale. In astronomy, we hear of stellar objects known as "black holes," visible only as dots of utter darkness. A collapsed star in the center has shrunken to a point so dense that its gravity lets nothing at all, even light, escape from its surface. There is an imaginary ring in space around such a black hole, referred to as the Schwartzchild radius, or the "event horizon." This is the outer limit of its swirling gravitational vortex, the dark whirlpool that can seize anything at all and whirl it into that darkness forever. When observing an object in space, if it were to slip over that event horizon, it would not just disappear immediately from our sight. As it approaches the rim, the vortex starts to suck in any reflected light. Massive time distortions begin to occur as it starts its timeless spiral to the invisible center. To any observer looking through a telescope, the object seems to reach the event horizon, and then suddenly freeze in place as it slowly fades away. The moment it fell over the edge, there was nothing left but the old image; everything else has already gone beyond, where human eyes cannot see.

If it were you there, your friends on earth would see you slowly disappear at the very edge of darkness, rather like the Cheshire Cat, perhaps with a last smile while you, now surrounded by your own light, in another time and space, are travelling forever into the center of brightness, into a final perfect union with perfect union itself, the solid, completely compressed brilliant stuff of the primeval universe. Nothing has returned from that journey; even stars wink out when they meet the event horizon. They are going to where we cannot follow, over the edge of darkness to the city of light.

Death, as we watch it, seems very much the same. We see our loved ones simply posed, as they were poised a moment ago, in their last visible form in this universe while in another, deeper, reality they have already started towards a true and timeless light. We on the outside could see eons pass before their journey will end or that light could fail. They are moving now into the timeless eternity that we left so long ago, and the journey will take them just about forever and not a moment less. The universe finally unfolds itself for us again in a profound return, like the return of the tide that sweeps us finally into the endless sea. It makes no difference if it takes five days or five minutes or five seconds. Time will stop for each of us.

As memories simplify we are greeted and accepted and passed backwards into places of greater and greater love; for who did not love us as infants? Back we spiral in time, days, months, centuries appearing between the moments of earthly time. We begin to circle endlessly into the center of the only universe we knew, our everlasting light, our welcome home. Suns, moons, stars; all can come and can go many times, and that light will never fail. We have never been that far away from eternity; we carry it with us all our years. It finally comes for us when it is time for time to transcend again in the clear light of death.

We have our time here and much to do. And then, we will return home again. We never expected most of what has come to us in this life; but this is one thing we can almost surely count on if we have any faith in logic and basic neuroanatomy. Otherwise, we may as well put our faith in any other religious belief since, allowing for cultural and historical variations, they all come to nearly identical conclusions. The great prophets of the past used legend and poetry to teach us how to live well, and how to die well. We have so much more power in this age of science that it is important to know that the best science we have still tells the same story.

We are born from eternity into the heart of love, we are each absolutely unique and ultimately universal; we are each of us now, and each of us is forever. Christian, Muslim, and Jew can praise the God of Israel for giving us such a blessed system, as well as a Prophet and a Saviour to show us how to use it. Hindu, Buddhist and Taoists can accept a neuro-dharma with ease. Karma is conserved, Nirvana is nearby, and going with the flow seems to take us naturally to the stars.

We become once and we never unbecome; we all experience life until we experience death, and it is death itself that will take us on our endless journey to our expected, and appointed, meeting with eternity. We are now and we are forever; we can bet on that with very good statistical probability, from everlasting to everlasting for sure. Our story will not be repeated, but it's a happy ending. We can have faith in that, and every reason to believe.